Angie was one of the first healers to be employed by the NHS at University College London Hospital (UCLH) 1999 to 2011. She has written two books previously, The NHS Healer 2004 (Virgin Books) and The NHS Healer Onwards & Upwards 2017 (Pegasus Books). Now, with her focus firmly fixed on dementia care, she is well-placed to make a difference to others on this very challenging pathway.

This is a work of creative nonfiction. The events are portrayed to the best of the author's memory. While all the stories in this book are true, some names and identifying details have been changed to protect the privacy of the people involved.

The MAGIC MAN and His DEMENTIA ADVENTURE

Angie Buxton-King

The MAGIC MAN and His DEMENTIA ADVENTURE

Vanguard Press

VANGUARD PAPERBACK

A CIP catalogue record for this title is available from the British Library.

ISBN 978 1 80016 979 1

Vanguard Press is an imprint of Pegasus Elliot Mackenzie Publishers Ltd.
www.pegasuspublishers.com

First Published in 2023

Vanguard Press
Sheraton House Castle Park
Cambridge England

Printed & Bound in Great Britain

For Graham, my love.

What the heart has once owned and had,
it shall never lose.
Of all the earthly music,
that which reaches the farthest into heaven is the beating
of a loving heart.

Henry Ward Beecher.

Special thanks to Olu who walked beside us for six months as a very special human being and carer.

Kelly who put the sparkle back in Graham's eye, nurse Alice, Rocky and the goldengirls.

CONTENTS

FOREWORD

I can remember the exact moment that I decided to write a book about dementia. It was Boxing Day 2017 and I was driving back to Cornwall in the dark from a disastrous 'family' Christmas with my husband, Graham.

We had just passed Exeter service station, when Graham suddenly opened the passenger door and attempted to get out of the car at seventy-miles-per-hour.

It was the grand finale of a horrendous Christmas holiday.

I swerved onto the hard shoulder, managing to save us both from disaster and laughed aloud at our situation as tears streamed down my face. I thought to myself; this is not funny, but actually is funny and I wonder how many other people are going through similar experiences today on this wet cold December day because their loved ones have dementia.

That is the moment that I thought our experiences might be able to help others.

This book will describe our own personal journey through dementia; don't worry, it will have laugh aloud moments, magic moments, along with more thought-provoking moments. I have also included helpful tips on what worked for us at different stages of the journey that may resonate with you but, do feel free to ignore them, if they do not align with your beliefs.

A final word for this foreword…

You will have many people say to you that this is the worst thing that can happen to you as a wife, mother, father, important other, but, trust me, it is not, you will cope and cope well and there will be life after dementia for you.

BEFORE DEMENTIA (BD)

Firstly, let me introduce you to Magic Man AKA Graham before dementia.

Graham was born in 1949 and we have been married since 2003 after meeting in 1999.

Much of what I know about Graham's early years has been gathered from conversations with Alan, Graham's father. Alan and Angie, his mother, adored Graham resulting in a child and subsequent man who was full of self-esteem and charisma.

Because of this bubble of love, in Graham's world, everything and anything was possible, and he expected and received warmth and love from most of the people he encountered throughout his life.

It is true to say Graham had and, despite dementia, does have a 'special quality' about him and this may well have been, in part, because he had been injured in an accident when he was ten-years-old. His brother, Michael, has told me a little about the accident and it is clear that it was a serious shock to them all as a family, when Graham was hit by a car and rushed off to hospital. Graham had sustained a head injury and was in hospital for several days before making a good recovery. Alan said you would not have noticed he was different after the accident but, by all accounts, he was subtly different. Often, when you nearly lose a child, they become 'special'. I have had experience of this with my son, Sam, and understand how it happens and how it happened for Graham.

It is worth noting that the accident was probably the first important blow to Graham's head that may have had a bearing on the long journey to where we are now.

Graham was an enthusiastic sportsman excelling at most things, but he became quite a star at football, apparently, he had a 'magic left foot'. As he got older, the balls got smaller and he loved golf until dementia took away the ability to keep count and converse with fellow players.

Alan attended most, if not all, of Graham's football matches and handed me a huge box of trophies and newspaper cuttings from those days before he himself died in 2013. The photo albums show Graham was playing football well into his mid-/late-twenties. This was, of course, back in the days when footballs were heavy, especially when wet.

You may have read, as I have done, about other footballers of his generation who went on to develop dementia in their later lives. Graham had been heading the ball for a decade in these conditions, which cannot have helped the initial blow to his head; sometimes two and two really do make four and I personally feel this was important in his subsequent dementia.

I know little else about his younger life other than he married his first wife, Linda, in his twenties and they had two children together, Lisa and Martin.

Employment came easily to Graham as he had a lovely manner that people warmed to. He had a kinetic memory; he only had to be shown once how to do something and then he could then repeat and teach others. He eventually created his own print company and ran that successfully for many years.

In his late forties, he discovered Reiki.

Reiki became the focus and love of Graham's life from that point on and, by the time we met in 1999, he was a well-known Reiki healer, teaching and working privately around the Watford area of Hertfordshire.

I met Graham because a mutual friend had spoken to me about Graham's work as a Reiki healer and teacher. I had trained as a Spiritual Healer, so I was curious to know how Reiki was different from the healing that I delivered. We arranged to meet and, when he turned up at my door, I was pleasantly surprised to see that he was not sporting the standard healer garb of open-toed sandals, long ponytail and flowing shirt but, instead, looked like any other fit sportsman of his generation.

We were friends for the remainder of that year and then, in 2000, we became a couple. I can see now that we were very lucky to have found each other as we have enjoyed a relationship that has brought out the best in each other. We have been fortunate that our time together has been a truly loving and mutually supportive relationship and we have both flourished within it.

I remember one memorable occasion when we were together in Asda in Watford when a young boy with his father came up to Graham and said, "Are you Graham King the footballer?" Both the father and his son were looking up at Graham as if they had met a superstar. Graham had a humility and magic about him at that moment that I was very proud of; the same charm and humility that attracted many people to him right up until the end of his life.

It was clear as I grew to know him better that he was used to being recognised and noticed; adoration was something he had always had in his life.

From the moment we joined as a couple in 2000, we both worked tirelessly to begin the process of integrating Reiki/Healing into the NHS where it is now being used as an adjunct to conventional medicine for cancer patients.

Graham's career within University College London Hospital (UCLH) as a Reiki healer began in 2001 and went from strength to strength. He became very well-known for his work with children and teenagers with cancer who named him 'magic man'. His work at UCLH was featured on a BBC 1 Inside Out programme in 2008 and Graham worked within the cancer unit for ten years. He loved his work and became an important member of the medical and nursing teams.

When I met Graham in 1999, his mother, Angie, was having regular Vitamin B injections to aid her memory. The injections were helpful until 2003 when it became obvious that her memory problems had escalated. It was then that Alan, her husband, was told that she had Alzheimer's.

Angie's reaction to the diagnosis was that she had no such thing! Not surprising really as she was already some way down the path and had lost the ability to understand what was happening to her brain or to realise that there were large gaps in her understanding.

As Alzheimer's is not classified as a hereditary disease, this may be of no consequence but it is certainly interesting.

Over the subsequent years, Angie King senior declined quickly and Alan cared for her at home until the last year of her life when, at eighty-six, he just could not manage anymore by himself and Angie went, first, into respite care and, then quite quickly, into residential care.

You really do have to develop a good sense of humour to cope with this disease and two of my favourite memories of Angie at this time are,

- Angie locking Alan out of the house and saying he was not her husband!
- Angie escaping from the residential home to be found halfway to her local Watford shopping centre with a fellow resident!

It was not quite so funny when Graham expressed the same sentiment to me some years later and began to leave home on a regular basis!

Angie died in 2010 because of a stroke in her sleep and, I think it is fair to say, we were all thankful that her struggles were over.

Our struggles, however, were just beginning.

Chapter 1

FORESIGHT

I am very fortunate in my life that I have the gift of foresight. I say fortunate, but sometimes I see what is coming when it is not such good news so a blessing and a burden perhaps…

As an example, before my son, Sam, became ill in 1995, I had a powerful dream that I was running up a mountain with him in my arms, knocking on the doors of mountain huts, begging someone to help me. Sam, aged seven, was diagnosed suddenly with Acute Myeloid Leukaemia a few months later.

I have always had inner promptings, some people would say I am just restless but, really, I get a 'feeling' in my body that time is short and my response to that 'feeling' has always been to live every day as if I don't have a tomorrow. When I get that feeling, I have an inner knowing that something is coming even if I do not know what it is. So, having got the feeling in 2008 but not quite knowing why, I said to Graham, "Is there anything you'd really like to do before we get too old to do it?"

He replied that he really wanted to live by the sea.

Because of this casual conversation and the 'feeling', we began looking at places to live by the coast and, in 2009; we made the decision to move from Hertfordshire to coastal Suffolk.

We successfully sold our house in Pimlico, Hertfordshire, and the Suffolk house-hunt began in earnest. At our first viewing of Holly Tree House, we were greeted by John, who had lived there for some thirty-five years. John took us inside and introduced us to his wife, Rita, who was sitting in a chair with her hat and coat on. Rita was tightly clutching her handbag as if ready to go out for the day; she very clearly had dementia.

John introduced us to Rita and told us very proudly that she had an MBE for services to business. Looking at her sitting there, I remember thinking that we could run but we could not hide from whatever was coming down the track towards us and had a strong sense I was looking at our future.

That might sound a little pessimistic but that is not how I was feeling. It just motivated me more to help make Graham's dream of living by the sea come true as soon as possible.

My personal way of coping with these insights when I get them is to note them with interest and then get on with my life. There is nothing worse for everyone, in my opinion, than to shut up shop and withdraw into yourself. Quality of life does not reside up that one-way street or, at least, it does not for me.

I could see that Holly Tree House was a money pit and I was not interested in buying it so, when Graham came into the room and excitedly said, "Shall we make an offer?" I was surprised, to say the least.

He loved the house, and I did not have the heart, having just had a glimpse of what was coming, to say no. A good friend of mine said later, "if you are going to let Graham make decisions, could it be about something less important!" Well, maybe, but no turning in the road is the wrong one if you approach it with a sense of adventure in your heart, in my experience.

The day we moved into Holly Tree House, I had the first alarm call that something was beginning to change with Graham when he woke up that first night screaming with pain, as his legs had locked in spasms. He was ill and was delirious and sweating along with the rigidity. We got through the night somehow and saw a doctor the next day, who said it was just one of those things.

We spent the next two years happily bringing Holly Tree House back to life. We completely renovated it, creating a garden where once stood a derelict tennis court. It was fun, kept us busy and there was no sign of any problems with Graham's memory.

Over those two years, Graham developed (because of wear and tear) a serious back problem. By the time he could not feel his toes in 2011, surgery was the only viable option and he underwent back surgery at the Norfolk and Norwich Hospital.

I have read since then that having a general anaesthetic is not necessarily helpful when you have memory problems but, of course, we did not really know we had a problem at that point. In any case, not having surgery would have meant Graham would have lost any physical quality of life that he had, so it was an obvious choice to go ahead with the operation, even if we had known.

The surgery was a success and Graham recovered quickly, aside from nerve damage resulting in a dropped right foot. He had 'coped' for so long with his back pain that irreparable damage had been done to his nerves. Neuropathy was now going to be part of his life, along with a dropped right foot.

It was during the year after surgery that I began to notice the first personality changes in Graham. He has always been an emotionally intelligent and empathetic husband and his placid and gentle nature was the stuff of legends, hence the moniker 'magic man'. Now, he was short-tempered and lacking in empathy. Not all the time, just every now and again.

Perhaps I would not have noticed if we had a 'normal' marriage, but we did not have a normal marriage. When one hurt, the other hurt and we could read each other's emotions and minds—there was no hiding place emotionally in our marriage.

So, when his personality changed, I thought initially, well, we have been together eleven years, perhaps this is just what I have to expect, but I didn't like it one little bit.

Over the next two years, Graham's father's own health declined and, in 2013 on Christmas Eve, he passed into spirit. He had told Graham and Michael that he was ready to go and he expressed the wish to be reunited with Angie, their mother.

Alan, along with many of his generation, was very proud that his boys would inherit on his death and, just as he had planned, they did.

Money can be useful as it can provide you with choices and the ability to change things in your life. Sadly, for me, one of the choices the new, developing personality of Graham wanted to make was to move from Holly Tree House to a house near a shop and a bus route. He was also attracted to having more bedrooms to enable more visits from his children and grandchildren.

I did not want to move; young families are busy and we did not have that many visits from Graham's family so it seemed a strange reason to want to move. With hindsight, I can see so many of these random decisions could be put down to dementia forming but, at the time, I just went with the flow. Not really my style but, hey, I reasoned to myself, something new is always good.

We set about looking half-heartedly for another house and, whilst doing so, it was obvious to me that we were now very clearly not on the same page together. In the past, this would not have been a problem, we would have reached a compromise but the new Graham did not want to compromise and life got pretty challenging.

Eventually, life was so miserable that I agreed to put the house on the market and I kept my fingers firmly crossed that no one would want to buy Holly Tree House. As luck would have it, the first people to view it; loved it and my fate was sealed.

We eventually found a house close by that ticked all the boxes on Graham's wish list and we moved in August 2014.

The next two years were very challenging at times and I really thought we were heading for the divorce courts. Essentially, Graham was beginning to act like a stranger and I no longer knew who he was. I also did not recognise the person I had to be in order to keep the peace. It was not bad all of the time but the lack of emotional connection and empathy was, slowly but surely, destroying our marriage.

I spoke to my sister-in-law about how things were and received the response, "marriage is hard work, isn't it?" Hmm, tell me something I do not know! I also knew that our marriage was not the problem at all. Relationships have their difficulties, but this was something 'other than that' and I could not quite put my finger on what was going wrong.

Eventually, Graham and I had a huge argument and he said he was going to look for a house to rent to enable us to live separately. Looking at his blank and cold face as he told me his plans, I knew something was really wrong as, previously, he would have been devastated if either of us had suggested this way of living, even a few years ago.

I suggested he might be depressed due to his lack of emotion over our impending split and he agreed to go and see his GP.

When Graham came home from that appointment, he could not remember anything that had been said and the first real knots of apprehension began to curl in my stomach. Some days later, a letter arrived from the GP who had obviously realised that Graham had some problems with memory and had arranged for a psychiatric nurse to come to the house to run through the memory test.

Graham scored twenty-nine on that first memory test; thirty is considered normal.

So, nothing much to worry about, you might have thought or, at least, we did. However, the nurse wanted Graham to attend a clinic in Lowestoft for more detailed tests. Graham was sixty-four at this time and the nurse said this was not young onset dementia just memory problems but she did arrange a routine brain scan.

Graham was a little subdued whilst all this was going on but was still displaying a level of detachment that was new to him and so strange to me. It was as if these tests and conversations were happening to someone else. He certainly was not putting two and two together and making four, as I most certainly was.

When the results came back from the scan and all was normal, I breathed a sigh of relief, all was well after all, wasn't it? Well, actually, it was not, as our relationship was still different, and my husband was different, very different.

I knew something was changing within Graham and that he was not consciously being a cold, detached husband. I just did not know what was wrong or, at least, I did not want to face my real thoughts on what the problem was.

In times of crisis, my coping strategy is always to gain as much knowledge as I can about whatever the crisis is. I did this with leukaemia when Sam, my youngest son, was diagnosed and I now set about doing the same for dementia.

My next coping strategy was to consider;

1) What do we want to do with the rest of our lives?
2) What do we need to do to achieve this?
3) Whatever we want to do, let's get on with it as soon as possible

One of the things I needed to do was to think about my future. As a 'WASPI' woman, I could not get a pension until I was sixty-six and that was some years away. The term 'WASPI woman' (women against state pension inequality) is the nickname given to those of us born in the fifties who will have to wait until we are sixty-six to receive any pension from the government. This delay in pension, coupled with what was now coming towards us, made me consider how I was going to earn some money.

I also contemplated for the first time the previously unthinkable thought that I was going to have to deal with being a widow at some point in the future. Yes, you might think I am jumping the gun here, but that is the reality of dementia so you might as well look it in the eye and face it head-on.

As a couple, we have always worked hard and improved the houses we have lived in, but we have never had much cash because of our divorces in the past. My initial thought was that I could create a holiday let and earn a small amount each year to help keep us going. Luckily, our house held the possibility of having an annexe as a holiday let within it but, sadly, initial enquiries soon ruled that option out, as the costs would be prohibitive. It then became obvious that we needed to move, once again, to a location where we could afford to buy with a let attached.

We looked around our immediate area but there was nothing in our price range available, so we sat down together and talked through our options.

Reality check;

1. Even with a bigger house, we only saw Graham's family maybe twice a year so the larger house was irrelevant.
2. Where we lived had no bearing on how often we would see them. At two or six hours' drive, the visits would be the same, maybe twice a year.
3. Time was running out for adventures so, if we had one last one in our sights, where would it be?

My advice;

- Be aware that, what may seem like a relationship problem, could be the start of dementia. Personalities change as the disease starts to bite and so it's worth checking out if there could be a medical reason for the changes in your relationship with others, before making a drastic decision such as divorce.

- Never put off a treat, a holiday or spending quality time together. Try very hard to live in the moment; to do so enables life to become richer and more meaningful. It is a good way to live and will leave you with fewer regrets later in life.
- Do not stop planning adventures, living and loving, just because you sense something might be coming down the track towards you.
- It really does not matter where you live or what you do so, if there is something you have always wanted to do, please get on and do it.
- This is the right time to get Power of Attorney in place, if you have not already done so.

Chapter 2

CHANGES

There seem to be two consistent themes in my life: challenge and change. I am fortunate that life prepares me well for most of the challenges that have come my way.

Before my son, Sam, was diagnosed with leukaemia in 1995, I had walked the 'no treatment can help route' with my mother who was diagnosed with ovarian cancer in 1987. This led me to read many books on how to help yourself when conventional medicine cannot help you and to me, ultimately, training as a healer. This became all really useful when Sam was then in the same boat in 1995.

In Graham's case, I have had training that is rather more intensive by working when I was younger in a variety of caring roles;

- Employed as an auxiliary nurse in a nursing home aged eighteen with Alzheimer's patients
- Employed as a carer in a dementia nursing home in 1991
- Employed as a carer in the community for dementia patients in 1993
- Employed as a carer support advocate for Age Concern in 1995

- Trained carers in community care in Norwich in 2012

Therefore, no complaining was allowed from me as all my training was in place as we set off on our new adventure.

To survive dementia as a carer, you may find it helpful to apply these three key principles to your new life; improvise, adapt and overcome. I make no apologies for stealing this from the military, as what you are going to go through will need the courage of a professional soldier to survive and survive it well.

You will also need to begin to develop these qualities;

- **Physical:** You will need strength, stamina, and flexibility.
- **Mental:** You will need the intellectual capacity to plan, prioritise, and apply yourself to the new tasks.
- **Spiritual:** You will need the resilience to deal with discomfort, emotional pain, and suffering while maintaining a positive frame of mind as far as possible to overcome the problems facing you.

Do not spend any time worrying that you are not up to the task; you are in it anyway and you will survive it. These are just useful things to know along the way.

After many hours of researching dementia, I have come to the understanding that the likelihood is that Graham had frontal lobe dementia. This matters very little really, as there is no treatment for any type of dementia; just drugs to help the patient and their families cope with the symptoms as they arise. Some drugs allegedly slow down the death of the brain but I think the jury is out on that one, from my experience.

Symptoms of Frontal Lobe Dementia (FLD) include;

Personality and behaviour changes… Tick

Acting inappropriately… Tick

Appearing selfish or unsympathetic…. Tick

Neglecting personal hygiene… Tick

Overeating… Tick

Loss of motivation… Tick

Language problems—speaking slowly, struggling to make the right sounds when saying a word, getting words in the wrong order, or using words incorrectly… Tick

Problems with mental abilities—getting distracted easily, struggling with planning and organisation… Tick

Memory problems—these only tend to occur later with FLD, unlike more common forms of dementia… Tick

Your loved one will have their own diagnosis but, even with the same diagnosis, no two journeys will be alike. We are all unique and your loved one's reaction to a rapidly shrinking brain will be unique as will your reaction to becoming a carer.

Some people love being a carer, others struggle a bit. I'd say I struggle a bit but I'm pretty good at it because, now I've accepted my role, I am adapting to my new life. If you yearn for what your life has been, it will destroy any happiness you might be able to enjoy together; because that life has gone.

Of course, you are human and you will not always manage it but we can cultivate new ways of living if we have to and this is one of those times to create a new way of living.

In any close relationship, there are times when you do not get on but, when someone changes their personality without any obvious reason and they are over fifty, I think this should carry an amber flag. Of the very least importance, they may be having an affair, be depressed, worried, etcetera... if none of these things apply, then consider memory problems.

As you have read, these changes began for us following back surgery but I just thought our marriage was going stale. Even with hindsight, there was nothing much to be done aside from trying to 'live in the moment'. If you have a wish list, my advice would be to start ticking off those wishes together as soon as possible, as your window of opportunity to do these things will get smaller and smaller as you travel along the pathway.

In 2016 we moved to Cornwall to help facilitate an income and, in my mind, to accrue funds for Graham's care in the future. Graham was excited about the move; we both enjoyed the planning and excitement as it gave us both something to focus on. I am a great believer in the power of distraction, distraction is not the same as denial but I also find denial quite useful at times.

The first concerning example of big change within Graham came in 2016 following our move to the South West when I had a minor collision with another car in the narrow lanes surrounding our home. Having arrived back home feeling a little shocked, I was met by Graham who was unable to show a flicker of emotion, support or concern for me. You will have your own example of this lack of empathy from your loved one and you may well feel angry, as I did at that moment until you realise later that they just cannot help it. They are no longer thinking or feeling about you in the way they once did. It is all about them now so we, as their loved ones, may just as well accept it and try not to take it personally.

I will not pretend that this will not be a challenge.

You will have begun at this stage to notice that you now have to do all the thinking for the pair of you, in this instant, it was how to sort the car repair, insurance, etcetera. You will get used to doing everything as the dementia increases but I found the middle stage one of the most challenging because your loved one looks the same and so you still expect them to be the same. However, they are not the same, their brain is rapidly shrinking and that means you have to step up.

It was following an incident that I began to consider fast-forwarding my plan to accrue a pot of money that I knew I would need for Graham's care in the near-future.

I decided to convert the garage at our home into a holiday let to generate income. We were fortunate in obtaining planning and project 'Sunflower Lodge' began.

It's worth saying here that no one anticipates their relationship being destroyed in this way. Some people express that they didn't sign up for this… and, of course, you didn't but here you are anyway and chances are you care enough or love enough to support the person with dementia as far as you can along the way.

If you have been fortunate enough to enjoy a good relationship with your loved one, then caring may be easier to do than if your marriage was already showing signs of breaking down.

Although both Graham and I are in our second marriage, there has never been a time since we met in 1999 that either of us has been interested in other people. It, therefore, feels like the most awful betrayal when something happens that makes you question that status.

Let's talk about inappropriate behaviour.

Tessa was my Pilates teacher and we all enjoyed a close friendship together since we arrived in Cornwall in 2016.

There was no warning for Tessa or myself that Graham's relationship with Tessa had changed in his mind and I did not see any warning signs when we were all together. Having said that, I suppose I had noticed some lack of inhibitions for a while. Things like, commenting on people's size in a loud manner whilst out in public, hugging friends a little differently… an analogue would be like having an embarrassing toddler in tow so that I never quite knew what he would do or what would come out of his mouth next in public.

Tessa was enjoying a cup of tea with Graham whilst I downloaded some photos of her for her new website when she appeared by my side in the office looking a little uncomfortable.

I sensed something was up and asked her whether she was okay and she said she would chat with me later outside.

I finished the photos and we all gathered at the door to say goodbye with Graham looking a little sheepish… which I thought was strange.

Anyway… off I go with Tessa, accompanying her to her car and she nervously told me that Graham had just asked her out for a drink.

I said, “What, all of us?” and she responded, no, he had made it very clear it would be just her and he had delivered the invitation with a wink…

I do not mind telling you my stomach turned over as a variety of emotions swept over me. Firstly, I felt sorry for Tessa, checked she was okay, and then anger, as I realised, I was going to have to go back into the house and ask Graham about this.

When I returned to the house, Graham was still looking a bit sheepish and I will be honest and admit that annoyed me even more as he clearly had some sense that he had done something wrong.

I’ve become quite good over the years at lulling husbands into a false sense of security and inviting them to talk, only to land on them from a great height when they have confirmed they have overstepped the mark. I know it is not very healer-like behaviour but, what can I say, I am human!

I called Graham into the office to look at the photos I had been working on and said casually, "Did you have a nice chat with Tessa?" Poor fella could not look me in the eye, so I continued, "Anything to tell me, Graham?" He said, no, without making eye contact with me so I let him have it! I told him what Tessa had told me and, at the time, he had enough cognitive function to try to say she had misunderstood him. That just made me madder and we spent a few frosty days until I had researched the problem on the dementia forums and found it to be a very common experience.

Understanding why it is happening and dealing with the emotions associated with inappropriate behaviour are two very different things and I struggled for a while with this aspect of dementia.

Your loved one may express this aspect of dementia in some other inappropriate way. It can manifest in a variety of ways; dressing inappropriately, touching themselves in public, sexual talk—you name it, all of these things are a possibility at some point in the dementia adventure.

I would recommend you take a look at the various online forums to see the wide variety of ways your darling other can embarrass the hell out of you.

Again, it is another loss.

- Loss of the relationship with the person you thought you knew.
- Loss of any hope of things ever being the same again in your relationship with that person.

- Loss of the future that you thought you had with the loved one.

I am afraid the solution is to try not to take it personally. Your loved one is not hurting you deliberately, it is the dementia, not them, that is destroying how things were.

Looking back too much, will make you sad and, looking forward too far, will make you sad, as loss is an inevitable part of the dementia journey. Be kind to yourself and let the old life drift away whilst storing good memories for the future whenever you can, start to live day by day and in the moment. Your life will be easier if you can do this.

A WORD ABOUT ONLINE FORUMS

When I first looked at the online forums specific to dementia, I did the classic lurking, reading other people's posts and gaining knowledge. After a while of this, I found them so depressing that, I decided they were not helpful to me, so I no longer looked at them unless I wanted to know something specific.

That is how I met Jane. Something about my posts made her feel we were marching to a similar drum, and she got in touch.

It was a huge blessing to me to have someone I could say the most private things about my feelings and know that I was being heard and understood.

Jane writes a blog about her husband's early-onset dementia. The blog is a refreshing reminder that there is a different way to travel this pathway, one of hope and positivity, that those of us who survive dementia will have a future when this particular journey is over.

That is an important message for anyone going through difficult times and, especially true, as we both became WITs (Widows in Training) together.

If I could wave a magic wand for you, dear reader, I would grant you the gift of being able to detach emotionally from your loved one.

This might sound harsh but, if you can manage to detach YOUR feelings, then you will be able to cope with the emotional rollercoaster of emotions as your loved one slowly but surely disappears from sight in any meaningful way. This does not mean detaching from love but to begin to learn how to love them unconditionally, which will make your life easier.

If you can do this, their lack of connection to you and their lack of empathy will be easier to cope with.

When we meet them where they are instead of where we want them to be, then your life will become calmer and so will theirs.

Personally, because both Graham and I have both worked as healers for many years, the lack of empathy has been a bit of a mountain to climb for me, as I miss the person Graham was very much. However, because of my healer training, I have grown to understand unconditional love and what it means. Beginning to experience this kind of love has truly been a gift to me.

The term **unconditional love** does not mean love without limits or bounds. It means, 'I offer you my love freely without condition.' This means that, when we offer our love, we offer it without the expectation of repayment. This is very relevant to our role as a carer. We will not get it right all the time because we are human, but we can try, and that is what I do, try.

Small bits of advice;

- Exercise was helpful at this stage, and I bought an indoor bike for Graham to use. There really was an improvement following a half-hour session on the bike. Walking together and using the bike definitely helped Graham.
- We also used herbal remedies and memory and focus pills. I am not sure that these pills and supplements helped much but it is always good to feel you are doing something to help yourself.
- As with cancer, happiness stimulates us and has immune system benefits.

  Being happy is possible if you live in the moment and make each day count.
- I gave Graham regular healing during this stage, and he loved it as he always has done. We can never know how much it helped him but it is a beautiful thing to have been able to share together.

Chapter 3

ADVENTURES ABROAD

Some of the changes over the early years with dementia were so subtle that we adapted seamlessly to them, other changes were more obvious and life-affecting.

In 2017, a year after our move to Cornwall, the changes began arriving fast and furious and, in late 2017, Graham was not very well at all in a physical sense, which, in turn, seemed to make the dementia worse.

I read somewhere that moving can be good for dementia as it stimulates the mind. I think for us for the first year or so, yes, it was good for both of us to have other things to think about rather than just wait for dementia to come and get us.

For me, as you have heard, there was another important reason for moving to Cornwall and that was for me to be able to run a business at home so that Graham could stay at home as long as possible with support from me. I know the journey of dementia well, having cared for others in various care settings when my children were small, and I knew that I needed to plan and, if possible, accrue a financial nest egg for any care that I needed to buy in later.

The house we moved to in Cornwall had one holiday let in situ, with the potential to create another in the garage. Having now brought the idea of a second holiday let forward with project 'Sunflower Lodge,' we both loved the idea that, when we did not have holiday guests staying, we could give the Sunflower Lodge away free of charge to cancer patients as an adjunct to our charity work.

This we did for a number of years and we both loved meeting families who needed to just be normal and enjoy Cornwall. It was a very rewarding thing to be able to do.

During this period, it became obvious that the pace of Graham's decline had quickened and I had to face the reality that our bucket list needed to be actioned as soon as possible if we were to enjoy some golden moments together.

A cruise had featured for some years on our list of things to do when we had the money. The plan had been to start the bucket list in five years' time when we could sell our home and downsize, but it was becoming obvious that I needed to get a move on.

Time was running out, I knew it but, of course, Graham did not.

This is one of the hardest things about being a spouse of a person with dementia; you will be, as I was, acutely aware of all the changes in your loved one whilst they are, very often, quite oblivious to their own mental decline. I know there are dementias where this is not so but, for Graham, this was true and, aside from a few sad moments when he was aware he was not as he had been, he remained the same old magic man inside his head.

One of these sad moments was when he had to give up golf; but they really were very rare, so a little blessing really.

Graham had his seventieth birthday coming up in 2019 so I thought we would plan the longed-for trip… a cruise to the Caribbean as a special event for his birthday to look forward to.

I set about researching the best trips at that time of the year (February) poured over dementia forums for information, spoke to good friends who had cruised for a number of years and researched travelling with dementia and thought, yes, we, or more accurately, I, can do this.

The anticipation of the trip was fantastic and I am very glad that we enjoyed a year of anticipation because the trip itself was a bloody nightmare!

First, alarm bells rang when it came to packing.

Graham loves clothes and has always been the peacock to my hen, if you know what I mean.

Therefore, when the time came to pack and Graham did not have a clue what to put in his suitcase or how to fold or pack clothes, I felt the first prickles of alarm. After thinking, shall I cancel, I thought it through and I realised it was too late now not to go, so we pressed on.

Finally, the great day came, and we set off for Gatwick airport.

We had booked into a hotel at Gatwick for the night before our flight and, that evening, we walked across to the terminal to arrange a special check-in for passengers who need more support for the following morning.

As we walked across to the terminal, Graham looked around him in amazement and said, "Wow! I have never been here before, have I? Where are we?"

We have had lots of adventures together with many trips beginning at Gatwick, so this was quite a shock to me, but I covered my surprise and reassured him that we were off on an adventure together like the old days.

In hindsight, we should never have gone but hindsight is not called the clearest of vision for no reason and we were at the airport, so we pressed on. I had one moment of panic that evening at the hotel and almost called home, where Tessa was dog-sitting for us, to say we were coming back but, instead, I took a deep breath and carried on.

It may not surprise you to know my mantra is 'fortune favours the brave.'

After a restless night for me, we were up early and we went through customs reasonably easily, using the fast track process for 'special people' like us… and on board we went.

If I say to you, the experience was like travelling with a six-foot toddler maybe you will have an idea of how awful the long-haul flight to the Caribbean was.

I knew it was a very long flight and we had the usual back-of-seat inflight entertainment system and inflight meals but, cast your mind back, to how travelling with a toddler is and you've got the picture of what our very long flight was like. We managed, of course, but I had just had my first real glimpse of what this special holiday was going to be like.

Boarding the ship in Barbados, I felt a sense of achievement; we had made it, all was going to be well and we could now unpack and relax. I reasoned to myself that we were now going to be in one place just as planned, so things should be easy, in addition, all food would be prepared for us, what could go wrong?

What went wrong was Graham went down with norovirus on the second day of the cruise. Graham was very sick and confined to our cabin for forty-eight-hours and, of course, by that time, I had contracted it so forty-eight-hours for me in isolation. No trip to the restaurants, no dressing up and no island visits.

There was one particularly memorable moment when I was confined to our cabin and I thought Graham might be able to make it out on deck for a swim. I drew him a map from my sickbed to the swimming pool and off he went. He found the pool, had a great time, and came back very pleased with himself.

The fact that he came back four hours later scared the life out of me but, unbeknown to me, Graham had got lost coming back to the cabin until our room steward spotted him and delivered him safely back.

On the final day of our luxury Caribbean cruise, we flew back to Gatwick from St Lucia.

Coming through customs at St Lucia was like Dante's version of hell.

Crowds of people rammed in together, people shouting in your face about security and no announcements of flights or departure gate signage.

It was truly hell, top that with dementia and… well, I aged a lot that trip!

I have drawn a mental blank over the flight back home and then the journey to Cornwall from Gatwick; I cannot think about it now without breaking into a sweat!

My advice to you then, dear reader, is try to get any special trips in early and not take them later when the enjoyment level is virtually nil.

Just do not do it!

Safely back in Cornwall, peace was restored to our lives, we were back with our beloved dogs, and everything went back to our new normal.

The trip, having been such a disappointment, I gathered my courage and decided later on that year that we would have one last go at a flight and holiday.

I was determined that Graham would get a last holiday in the sun that he could enjoy so, in November 2019, we went to Tenerife.

What could go wrong? We could fly from Exeter (a dementia-friendly airport) and be in a hotel with everything on tap. I would highly recommend the dementia-friendly airports; it all worked brilliantly and the whole holiday was a much better experience, although not without its challenges.

One of them worth sharing with you is the amazing buffets provided for our meals.

Everyday choices are a problem when you have dementia, so a massive amount of choice at mealtimes completely confused Graham and eating became an ordeal rather than a pleasure. To manage the stress of Graham choosing his own meal, I escorted us both around the buffets, with Graham pointing out what he fancied and then, he waited at our table while I went to collect both our meals.

We managed and it was a much better holiday than the cruise had been and, yes, if you were a happy flyer yourself, you would be able to manage it and make a few golden moments to look back on, so I would advise you to go for it.

One caveat is to consider the airport at your destination as it may not be dementia-friendly. Tenerife was fine; the staff at the airport recognised the badge Graham had been given to wear at Exeter airport, and the staff were helpful.

It was a success of sorts and, seeing Graham swimming in the pool at our hotel, was a magic moment for sure.

After Tenerife, I took the decision not to take any more trips with Graham because, as the dementia continued, he found being in unfamiliar territory very disorientating so it really would not have been worth it.

Once again, it is similar to travelling abroad with small children; the disruption of the flight, strange food, strange rooms may not be worth the effort you put in to get there.

I am glad that I have many, many memories of great times together in our favourite destination of the Greek Islands where we hired scooters and explored together free as birds. We have been lucky and I have my memories, even if Graham does not.

My advice;

- Do not leave it too late to do things.
- Plan like a soldier for anything you intend to do and realise that you are in charge of filling in the gaps in every way now.
- If you do not want to go on a trip, then do not attempt it. Whilst it is tempting to think, it is all about the person with dementia, it is not, and you matter too.
- This goes for families too. If it is difficult to have them visit, then do not do so. It is not your job to make life easier for other family members; you have enough to cope with.
- Chances are all the efforts you are making to bring people together will no longer be viewed as important by your person with dementia anyway, so go easy on yourself.

Chapter 4

FAMILIES

The 'invisibles' is a term used on dementia forums and elsewhere to describe the surrounding families of dementia patients.

Harsh?

Well, maybe, and of course, this is not true for all families but, for far too many of us, it is the cold reality as the dementia journey bites. Never more keenly is this felt than around the Christmas holidays.

It is true when people say that you find out who your true family are when you have a diagnosis of dementia or indeed a difficult diagnosis of any kind.

There are probably a variety of reasons why families and friends keep away when dementia or serious illness strikes and it is not my role here in this book to explore the subject matter too deeply. Safe to say that the people who have been there for us as a couple and maybe for you too will surprise you, as they may not be the people you might have expected them to be.

I have found personally that, when the person with dementia (as well as in my case, the carer), is no longer able to be the person they once were to another family member or friend, then that's when the people who you may have thought would have been there for you, are not.

I felt sad initially for the family members and friends that did not take advantage of precious years, months, hours, with Graham as he travelled down the road of dementia. Then I realised I did not have the time or the energy to rescue these people from their own future and I chose instead to focus on making the most of each day and making life as good as it could be for Graham.

Everyone has their own problems, of course, but if you have one or two close friends that are there for you, whether that be in person, on the telephone or via the internet, hold them close as they will keep you sane when life gets really tough.

Rest assured, that there will be people who will step forward to walk alongside you and new valued friendships will be formed.

The last big family Christmas gathering in Hertfordshire was a total disaster.

We had been invited up to stay for a 'special Christmas' with Graham's family. Graham has two children from his first marriage with four grandchildren. Life is busy for people with young families and, therefore, we do not see his family very often. I do try to keep them informed of his wellbeing and condition but, sadly, there was a complete lack of awareness of how he really was and what could reasonably be expected of him in the upcoming family Christmas.

Maybe they were in denial.

It is a five-hour drive from Cornwall to Hertfordshire and en route Graham asked repeatedly where we were going and why it was taking so long to get there. Service comfort stops led to more confusion, as Graham had no idea where we were and just wanted to go home. Despite the challenges en route, we arrived in St Albans in time to meet his family and two of the grandchildren for the carol service at St Peter's church… so far so good.

I had to leave the dogs in the car when we arrived but I thought they would be fine as I offered them a toilet break several times along the way.

We made our way to the church where Graham's family were meeting us. I had thought they would be saving us a seat, but no seats had been saved, so we sat separately and waved at them across a crowded church.

After the service, I left Graham with his family to make the last five-minute journey to their house and I went to collect our car from the car park.

When I opened the driver's door, Alice, my little Jack Russell was in the driving seat… she had climbed through the car, spreading a runny tummy all over the contents of a packed Christmas car… Argh! If this was a sign of the upcoming Christmas experience, as it happens, it was an accurate one and I should have taken more notice of it and hightailed it back to Cornwall there and then.

I cleaned up as best as I could and, with the windows down, drove to the house to meet up with Graham and his family.

I knocked at the door, went in to explain what had happened and to collect some paper towels to clean up the mess, half hoping someone would offer to come and help me.

Silly me.

My host sat in his office where he could see me unpacking all the suitcases and presents and, only when his wife suggested he offer help, came out as I was finishing to say, whilst standing well back, "Anything I can do to help?"

It has often been said that with me what pops into my head comes out of my mouth but happily for him, not this time!

Into the house I staggered with our two dogs and all the bags and gifts and took a big breath to steady myself.

Graham's grandchildren were very happy to see us both so that was a bonus; sweet little things.

I was told that a close friend of theirs was coming to supper to see us… oh, happy days, more confusion for Graham… and no consideration for his condition. Graham had no recollection, of course, of meeting this 'close friend' before so it was not an easy supper.

I won't bore you with the details of what happened next, but a conversation took place between the 'close friend' and me that resulted in my step son-in-law saying to me, "my house, my rules."

I felt the blood rush to my head and thought to myself, 'I've fallen into an Alf Garnet sketch' and responded by laughing out loud and replied calmly, 'I understand completely.'

For the second time that day, it was a good thing my mouth seemed to be jammed shut. My instinct, of course, was to pack up and stay in a hotel that night but I knew I could not do that because it would cause further confusion for Graham so I inhaled deeply and gave a performance worthy of an Oscar for the next twenty-four hours.

No one, aside from 'my house my rules' and I knew what had taken place that Christmas Eve and the whole of Christmas Day on the surface was a success.

By the time Christmas day was over, I could not keep it up any longer and said I felt it would be easier if we travelled back to Cornwall on Boxing Day rather than the following day as planned.

I had done well and I had made it this far without exploding, but I knew I could not make another day without exploding and the last thing I wanted to do was to spoil the childrens' Christmas.

I packed up, we left for home and, quite honestly, I have never been more relieved to leave anywhere. As I drove home, I vowed to myself that I would never, ever do that again.

I have written in the foreword the experience of Graham opening the car door on the M5 on the way home but, for me, it felt like a fitting ending to, what I now refer to in my mind as, the Christmas from hell.

So, in summary, my advice to survive Christmas would be… do what works for you, as your person with dementia will not care where they are, as long as you are beside them. Do not, whatever you do, put up with a Christmas for others that will be hell for you as I did; it is not worth it.

Christmas for us as a couple all but disappeared in the last three years of dementia.

A new type of Christmas could still be enjoyed initially but, then… oh, how things changed.

The last good Christmas we had as just the two of us, was when we were still living in Cornwall and I was very aware at that time of experiencing a lot of anticipatory grief, which, in itself, was very painful. Graham's lack of cognitive function, lack of empathy and, sadly, lack of speech were difficult to witness. He was there in the physical sense but not in any other sense. I did a fair amount of crying that year, as I was very aware that I was alone in everything I did to prepare for the holiday and that next year would be even worse. That said, Christmas became easier after that, as I had largely let go of any expectations that things could be as they were.

The following Christmas, I had no expectations at all. I successfully bought, transported home and put up a beautiful seven-foot tree myself and we were invited next door for Christmas lunch… perfect!

I found being just the two of us alone, far easier to cope with and Graham has no memory of his family most of the time so did not miss them in any noticeable way.

What I have personally found at Christmas and high days is that I experienced a lot of anticipatory loss; I felt as alone just as surely as if Graham had already passed to spirit. That was tough to experience.

I believe I am fortunate though as, when things are difficult, I always have the experience of losing my son, Sam, when he was ten to leukaemia to measure things against and I can honestly say that whatever I am experiencing with Graham, does not compare at all with the grief of that.

This next bereavement, when it comes, will be after Graham has lived a full and colourful life and at the right age when someone may reasonably expect to have some illness or another. It is completely different.

My advice;

- Earlier in the journey, all family members will benefit from making time to spend with their father, mother, etcetera, as these will be remembered as golden memories for everyone left behind after the person with dementia is safely in spirit.
- Every family will be different but I would avoid all stressful family occasions as your person with dementia will get very agitated at all the changes, activities and who now seem like strangers talking to them.
- Christmas is going to be tough for you. There is no way around it, I am sorry, but that is the reality for us, carers.

Chapter 5

LET US TALK ABOUT SEX

Now I am not a great one to talk about sex but it does form part of most people's lives, marriage or relationship and so I need to chat about it, as this aspect of your life is definitely going to change.

There are many ways of looking at these changes and, it is fair to say, I have shed some tears over the years about some of the changes that have occurred since dementia came into our lives, but I have also laughed aloud at some of the changes. As an example, if I forget and say something a little too personal and fruity to Graham, he looked at me with a look of astonishment and horror that I could be so naughty and I am sure, to his mind, over-familiar. This is because, to him, I am not his wife but someone who is being far too personal with him! I find this very amusing.

I remember attending a meeting at a support group (when such things were possible pre-covid) and hearing the testimony of one woman who was devastated as her husband had been affected badly in this aspect of their lives together.

Not because of the loss of sex but, rather, that her partner now had an insatiable desire for sex. I remember thinking then, bloody hell I am lucky, as that would be so much worse to cope with than the desert we have in our lives. A hidden blessing perhaps!

We have been married nineteen years and together for twenty-two years at the time of writing and, in that time, we have enjoyed many wonderful times together. Or, more accurately, we enjoyed some wonderful times for twelve years of that time with plenty of good times in the second decade as well, but… Well, you know what it's like, don't you, dear reader?

It is all too easy for our memories to make the past better than it actually was. Having dementia for years before being diagnosed, means that you may have been aware of changes happening in this area of your life that, like me, you have put down to married life and its many nuances.

I do get a little tetchy when professionals say to me, 'Oh, he is still the person you knew and he is still in there somewhere.' Well, I can tell you at that time in the middle stages of the disease, he most definitely was not. There is a new Graham that I love unconditionally but the old Graham has gone and, as brain cells cannot regenerate, he is not coming back.

Depending on the type of dementia your person has the changes will be different. In Graham's case, he has more of the frontal lobe dementia symptoms with the accompanying emotional detachment. This is hard to take within a marriage, especially my own, as I have enjoyed many years with a person who was extremely emotionally intelligent. Because Graham has little to no empathy and now has no emotional connection to me, as he thinks he is twenty-eight and I'm an old woman, we both feel less and less connection to each other and then, of course, the sexual desire decreases.

However, let's back up a bit.

When Graham had his back surgery in 2011, there was some residual nerve damage that left him with a dropped foot and neuropathy.

You have read earlier that having an operation with a general anaesthetic may accelerate dementia if it is waiting in the wings.

We had a follow-up appointment with the orthopaedic consultant at Norwich on the same day as we had the first memory test, so I was already feeling a little fragile when we were wheeled in to see the young consultant.

Graham asked the consultant about sexual activity, explaining he was experiencing a few problems and the young buck consultant casually looked up at us (clearly thinking), 'what are these old folk asking me that question for?' and said, "Oh, that probably won't happen naturally now but we can suggest a variety of things…"

There was no response from Graham to this but the nurse in the room must have seen my expression, as she came outside with us as we were leaving and hugged me, saying, "I'm sorry, he has a lot to learn about his consultation style."

I was very upset but did not actually know why but, in hindsight, I think it was just another unwelcome reminder that life had changed and was going to get worse, not better.

Now, I have accepted dementia, I know and understand that the neuro pathways are not connecting in a variety of different ways and, therefore, this aspect of life is affected just as every other aspect will be eventually, but in the beginning, it is tough.

Understanding that they are no longer the person you fell in love with and married is hard and a form of letting go that you will fight against, to begin with, but, if you can begin to let the old personality go, you will be happier and, surprisingly, so will they.

So let us fast forward for a moment.

Sitting while having coffee with Graham one morning, I saw for the first time a look in his eye that I had seen in many dementia patients' eyes in the past. He did not know who I was.

I had known this moment would come and, for us, it coincided with a sudden increase in paranoia in Graham's behaviour.

Once I had seen this look, many of the challenging aspects of Graham's behaviour clicked into place for me.

One of them relating to our subject matter was that, if he did not recognise me then when we went to bed at night, he had no idea who the woman was he was getting into bed with.

I got out some old photo albums and flicked through them casually (as the professionals tell you to do) until we came to the photos of us getting married.

He pointed himself out and then looked bewildered at the person standing next to him.

I said, "That's me, Graham." His response was to burst out in childlike giggles saying, "Don't be silly, you're an old woman!"

It really was very funny. However, click, click, click went my brain and shatter went more pieces of my heart.

As the day passed, I asked a few pertinent questions such as, are you married? What age are you?

His response was, no, he was not married, and he was twenty-eight.

Ah, ha, I got it.

So, we had a chat and I suggested if we were not married, perhaps he would like his own room and wardrobe.

His eyes lit up with excitement and he clearly loved the thought of independence, so we set about making a new place for him in the spare room upstairs.

He was delighted with our new arrangement and became very settled for quite some time. It seemed Graham was happy to live with me but much happier that we were not sharing a bedroom.

How did I feel?

Well, I spent a fair few nights crying myself to sleep and adjusting to this new reality, but then the advantages kicked in, as I now began to sleep soundly for the first time in a long time. There is always an unseen gift if we can just see it!

A few weeks later, whilst watching TV together, Graham kept looking over at me with a glint in his eye and then with a cheeky grin said, “I think I might join you in your bedroom tonight, if you’d like me to?”

What to say?

There was enough of the old Graham sitting in front of me to say, yes, that is fine, imagining that we would indeed just go to sleep together.

The cheeky grin got wider as we snuggled up together and kisses were exchanged, which made me very aware of what I had lost but I also knew, absolutely knew, that Graham was kissing someone that he didn’t know. That was not a good feeling at all. I could literally have been anyone; he was just attracted to me that evening and acted on it.

The next day, he had no recollection of any intimacy, and I knew that, for me, that was the last time I would allow that to happen.

In truth, he never initiated coming into my bed with me again anyway until much later that year when he asked me to marry him.

Now, that was a magic moment.

Graham had fallen in love with a new woman (me) and wanted to marry me. I chose to view his proposal as a compliment. Although he had no idea who I was, he felt enough of a connection to me and the life we were sharing to want to make a new connection with me. We talked about how we would get married in many of our conversations, until his memory had declined further, but we had some fun discussing honeymoon locations and such-like before that decline happened.

Graham's emotions would swing back and forth during this time, sometimes within a few hours; from being tearfully emotional and expressing great love for our life together, to paranoia when a surprise visitor came, or the postman delivered mail and flicked the switch in his brain.

We would laugh a lot together and I have these moments stored in my 'golden memories file' for the future' and, in the next moment, Graham would be in a dark sulk about some perceived hurt.

It is hard not to swing back and forth with your loved one but, if you can just hold steady to your own emotions and know without a doubt that it is the dementia playing these tricks on you and not your loved one, you will be doing really, really well.

Life is indeed a funny old thing and it does not get much stranger than when dementia comes to stay.

My advice;

- Try hard not to take things personally. You will not always succeed but the more you can do this, the easier your life will be.
- If you are hurt, your energy and your body language will change towards your person with dementia and then they will react negatively.

- As their cognitive ability declines, they rely more and more on body language to gauge how people are with them. If your body language is off, they will react angrily to reflect you.
- Do look at the Teepa Snow YouTube videos as she role-plays these unhelpful exchanges very well.
- Read Contented Dementia by Oliver James… it is a lifesaver.
- You are probably thinking that you are being asked to be something you did not sign up for. Yes, you are but, unless you are going to leave the care to someone else, you need to make it as easy as possible for yourself.
- Healing really helps with the agitation, it calms with the touch of love and compassion just when they need it and when words will just not do.

Chapter 6

DIAGNOSIS

To diagnose or not to diagnose, that is the question.

We had our first medical appointment in 2015, some two years after I had first noticed personality changes occurring in Graham. This reluctance to seek advice from the medical world was Graham's decision but I supported him in his decision, as I knew that was one of his ways of coping. I know from my work with carers in the past that having repeated memory tests is not always very helpful to either the patient or the carer. To put it bluntly, you do not get better at these memory test appointments, you get worse. This is not really a helpful or a positive measure for a patient struggling to function.

So, if no doctors were what Graham wanted, I was happy to support him in that decision, as I personally feel it makes very little difference to the outcome.

However, moving to Cornwall and, after further obvious decline, I suggested that Graham might like to chat to the doctors as his mood seemed low. The result of that consultation was, "no need to worry, old chap, everyone has these memory problems from time to time."

At the time, I was irritated that Graham had not been supported better or signposted to some support but, in hindsight, I can see that the GP had judged Graham well and that Graham's preferred route of doing nothing suited him well.

Because we had moved home, we had to carry out many DIY jobs and I increasingly began to notice that Graham could not understand written instructions very well and was no longer able to do simple household tasks.

We had by now embarked on 'project Sunflower Lodge' and this meant making decisions on a variety of things. Decision-making was something that became increasingly problematic as the dementia worsened. This stage was very difficult to manage as, if I made too many decisions myself, it felt like I was cutting Graham out but asking him to make decisions caused him stress and that made his dementia symptoms worse. Faced with the facts, it began to be clear just how much I had been 'filling in the gaps' to try and make the transition easier for us both.

This is the stage of the journey where you, the carer, have to 'upskill' so you can do these things yourself. I cannot recommend YouTube tutorials highly enough as I can now attempt most simple tasks DIY as long as I've watched the videos first!

In the beginning, it frustrated me that I had to do the jobs that had always been Graham's domain. I could not do them very well, so I got very irritated but now, years later, I get a real sense of achievement if I rewire a plug, change a tricky light-fitting or change a loo seat. For his part, Graham did not seem to mind me doing the chores that used to be his responsibility, he just seemed relieved he did not have to do them.

There is no point at all in you feeling resentful, as I did occasionally, as your person with dementia cannot do these things anymore so it was my job, however challenging, to take the lead and to accept that I had to do them or pay someone else to do them for me!

During this period, Graham's speech began to decline rapidly and I now know this is called expressive dysphasia and Graham's expressive dysphasia was significant.

This meant that golf was no longer possible for Graham and he found it hard not to be able to carry on with his game as he missed the social contact that golf offered him. Various people tried to reassure him that they would support him on the golf course but it seemed, if he could not play to the standard he was used to, then he did not want to play at all.

Up until this point, we had continued to deliver our charity's training, 'Healing in a Hospital and Hospice' together as we loved teaching others. Our teaching styles were very different, making the courses a hoot for the students and us. There was much hilarity all round during our comedy routines. We deliberately included humour in the training, as the subject matter can be a little heavy until you get used to it.

Graham has always been a slow and deliberate thinker and speaker and, over the next few years, I became adept at filling in the blanks for him and he increasingly looked to me to do so. After a while, though the pleasure had gone out of teaching for Graham, I carried on spreading the word by myself with his full encouragement.

I remember one unhelpful family member telling me at the time they did not think there were any issues with Graham's speech… I just talked for him! Ouch.

In fact, Graham's loss of speech has been one of the worst aspects of his dementia for us both as it was so very difficult for him to express and so difficult for me to understand what he was saying or needed. Happily, Graham was rarely distressed by any of his other symptoms at that time and seemed to take it all in his stride. He retained his sunny nature for the most part, just occasionally lapsing into frustration.

Around this time in late-2017, I saw a Facebook advertisement asking for people with cognitive difficulties to join a clinical trial which was being run locally for patients in Plymouth. Having worked in the NHS for some time, I knew that such trials could be useful, as they usually meant you received attention that is a little more personal. I persuaded Graham that perhaps it would be a good thing to participate in the trial, saying that if the new drug they were using was of use it might be worth finding out more.

We made the appointment and drove to Plymouth to see the consultant.

How wrong could I have been; it was a horrendous, torturous experience!

I think it is reasonably common when you live with people not to realise how bad a problem is until someone else sees them with different eyes.

When we arrived for our consultation, Graham was taken into a separate room and asked many questions (the usual memory test) and had a score of twenty-one… so quite a long way from the twenty-nine he had scored two years previously.

This meant we did not tick their particular box for the trial. This was not in itself a problem, we would just go home, I thought. However, no, the consultant said if Graham would take another test then he would be able to place him on a slightly different trial.

Before taking Graham off to take this new test, the consultant, without any warning and completely out-of-the-blue, told us that he was making a working diagnosis of Moderate Alzheimer's disease and asked Graham if he would like to take some drugs to attempt to slow the process.

I could see that this sudden diagnosis had hit Graham for six and that tears were beginning to well up in his eyes. They were welling up in mine too but mainly because I was so angry at the callous and brutal way the diagnosis had been delivered.

Reeling from the shock of this abrupt diagnosis, Graham was then whisked away for the second memory test and scored even lower… no surprise there, as he had just been delivered a body blow. This, however, meant he could not be entered on any trial. Talk about a double whammy; it was brutal.

This dreadful way of breaking bad news needs to change. I have seen too much of it when people are diagnosed with cancer and, here I was, seeing the same bad practice in dementia care. We ended the consultation and drove home with Graham an emotional heap beside me. In the end, we pulled over on the side of the road and held each other tight, weeping together. It was heart breaking.

It was not the diagnosis that broke my heart but the way it had been done. No blood test, no brain scan and not a jot of compassion, just brutal words.

If I tell you I wrote a strong letter of complaint, I am sure you will not be surprised, and I received a response with the usual platitudes of "lessons will be learnt."

The result of this entire trauma, of course, meant that Graham never wanted to see a doctor again.

Crying done, we managed to adjust back to normal life and carry on as before.

During this time, our wonderful friend, Alex Bonney, came to visit us in Cornwall as he was making an up-to-date short film about our charity's work. Alex and his wife, Claudia, who worked as a healer at Bristol's Children's Hospital (as part of one of our charity's projects,) both gave their expertise and time freely and we will be forever grateful to them. It would have been lovely to include Graham speaking in the film but, sadly, it was not possible because of his speech problems. What was possible, though, was for me to arrange a recording studio at Truro for Graham to record four meditations that accompanied my book about our charity's work in the NHS entitled Onwards and Upwards. I am so glad we did this as I can sit and listen to Graham's beautiful voice anytime I want, captured for all-time.

In October 2018, our charity received an award at a very glamorous function in London. It was wonderful for our work to be recognised but so sad that Graham was unable to really understand what was happening or what we had achieved together. Without Graham's support and love to keep me balanced and grounded, I doubt we would have created our charity at all. It is a wonderful legacy to leave for other healers who wish to work in the NHS to follow, should they wish to do so. We have both been very touched to be able to help so many cancer patients and their families since the charity was created in 2006.

Our charity was the overall winner of the Complementary Therapy Awards and the winner in the cancer category. The awards sit proudly in our office and I have very special memories of that day, even if Graham does not and it is a wonderful reminder of all that we have achieved together.

It seems to be a bit of a pattern with dementia that, following a fall or a heavy cold, the dementia takes a deeper hold. Graham developed further cognitive and speech problems which increased the stress both for him and for me during this time following a fall at home.

It was time for a serious think about where we should live, as the dementia progressed and we made the difficult and big decision that our future lay back in Suffolk. We had always thought we would stay for five years in Cornwall and then return to Suffolk but I/we thought the time to return had to be brought forward.

At this point, Graham still remembered some of our friends in Suffolk so he was happy to feel we were making the move back.

I told him it might take time but that we would go back in the next few years,

When I say, 'we thought', that is not true as I was, by now, having to make all the decisions in our lives. Some people may have thought 'incorrectly' in the past that I have always made the decisions in our house, but that is not the case. Graham has always been very articulate in having his say about the direction of our lives and it was a transition period as I, slowly but surely, had to pick up the reins by myself. Having to decide all the big important life-changing events by myself was initially a very lonely experience but, happily, I soon got the hang of it!

We have a close network of friends in Suffolk, and I knew I would need the comfort of friends going forward. 'Friends are the family we choose for ourselves,' they say and that is certainly true of our friends in Suffolk. I am also fortunate to have, who I now know is, my soul family, Liz Weir is a wonderful soul sister to me, often unseen but always there at the end of a phone to support me.

Having made the decision to move back to Suffolk sooner rather than later, we put our home in Cornwall on the market to let fate decide if this was the best plan or not.

We had no luck at this first attempt at selling so I had no choice other than to revert to plan B. Plan B was to try to get a live-in carer in whilst we were still in Cornwall to help us continue to manage at home. The problem would be how we would afford it if we could not sell the house.

Life was busy, very busy. I was still running the house and the two holiday lets along with our charity. It was becoming very apparent that I was not able to supply the entire stimulus that Graham now needed as golf had gone from his life. I knew that I needed help to give Graham the quality of life that he deserved and, if this meant getting a formal diagnosis, then, so be it.

Therefore, in August 2019, two years after our appalling appointment in Plymouth with the dementia consultant, I encouraged Graham to seek a formal diagnosis via our local GP to find out what help was available to us. We saw a different GP this time and he immediately referred us to Bodmin Memory Clinic.

One of the great benefits of finally seeking a formal diagnosis was the introduction that followed to the local mental health team and our local memory café.

It was initially disappointing to experience that the appointment at the memory clinic was exactly like the disastrous visit to the clinical trial in Plymouth.

There were endless questions that Graham did not have a hope in hell of answering, due to his speech and cognitive abilities. This resulted in a very frustrated and anxious Graham, whose only way to express his displeasure at the process was to become angry, very angry, which was not a very nice experience for either of us. On a lighter note, I had to smile ruefully to myself when the consultant said to Graham, “if you remember just one thing today, remember you have dementia!” You have to laugh!

Because of our visit to the memory clinic, the consultant agreed to a brain scan at the hospital in Truro. I wanted Graham to have a brain scan to ensure no stone had been left unturned and to make certain there was no other reason for Graham’s now-rapid decline.

The brain scan came back as normal, the same as the one we had in Suffolk in 2014. Make of that what you will.

Sadly, one of the unwanted side effects of a formal diagnosis meant that Graham could no longer drive. It was one of the worse things that Graham had to go through at that time, and he was very, very cross about it for a long time. In the end, I sold his car so the temptation was taken away; you can imagine I was not popular for doing so.

As the carer, you are now being stretched in many different ways. If anything needs acting on quickly then the only person able to react quickly is you, which is not without its challenges.

Three examples from this time are;

We had holidaymakers in the Sunflower Lodge and they knocked on the door early one morning to tell me there was sewerage coming up through the shower trap. OMG! I had no idea what to do and Graham stoically carried on eating his poached eggs on toast whilst I ran around like a headless chicken.

A friendly plumber, who wasn't able to call personally, talked me through what I had to do. So, with drain rods firmly in hand, I lifted the manholes as instructed to find the blockage.

You can imagine what I saw, and I thought, 'good lord! What has my life come to?' I am now rather proud to own my own set of rods and, furthermore, I know how to use them.

Then we had a chimney fire.

I could hear the fire raging in the chimney and shouted to Graham for help with, of course, no response but, luckily, instinctively, I put out the fire in the grate, shut off the air supply to the fireplace and waited for the fire engine to arrive.

"What fire?" said Graham.

Lastly, was a huge wasp nest in the attic.

I could see that there was a mark on the celling upstairs and I gingerly put my finger against the mark to see what was causing it. My finger went straight through the ceiling and a wasp fell out. The air turned blue as I yelled for Graham to help, with no response (I'm allergic to bees and wasps) so I grabbed some loo roll and some tape, sealed the hole and waited for my neighbours to get home to ask for advice.

There was a nest in the attic that stretched the length of the house along a beam and the juice from their mouths had rotted through the plaster.

Oh, and then I forgot about the swarm of bees that came to live on the wall outside our patio doors.

Phew! After a while, these things no longer bothered me, it was just one more thing to triumph over. Hidden gifts to me, as I began to be able to cope independently, which all helped me to cope after Graham passed away.

At this point, I was doing a lot of research; reading many books about supplements and diets that might help. Frankly, it is a little like helping yourself with any disease; it's empowering to educate yourself about other people's journeys but then be selective about what you do in your own lives and only do the things that you feel guided to. I feel that anything you can do to be proactive and help yourself is probably a good thing as, placebo or not, Graham was functioning pretty well considering we were now quite advanced on our adventure with dementia.

Graham willingly took;

- Turmeric
- Memory focus pills
- Vitamin C

My advice;

- Think carefully about seeking a diagnosis unless you feel it can help you in some way.
- For example, if you need some support, financial or emotional then, yes, a diagnosis will help, otherwise it is a huge hammer blow to be diagnosed with something that there is currently no cure for.
- Be led by your person with dementia until you have to take control of all aspects of their lives and

then you are free to decide if a diagnosis will now help you in some way or not.

- Research local support services in your area.
- If you do not qualify for any outside help as we did not, then start planning how you are going to pay for some private help to come in to allow you some free time.
- This is where a diagnosis comes in, as you can then apply for attendance allowance and carer's allowance. These two allowances paid for help at this stage in our journey.
- I know I'm repeating myself but make it easy on yourself, practise acceptance

Chapter 7

SUPPORT AT LAST

Because of our formal diagnosis, we were referred to the community psychiatric nurse in our area. Gerard came to visit us a few weeks later at home and Graham immediately took to him and his gentle caring manner.

Isn't that funny? I have just re-read this chapter and can see that I refer to the diagnosis as ours, not Graham's. Interesting that… I suppose I have always felt that we are in this together, always have been and always will be. There has never been any him and me, there is just us.

Gerard suggested that Graham might want to link in with the local memory groups in the nearby village of Lanivet and he provided us with pathways to local support groups that we could access in our own time.

Taking this step was a big deal emotionally for me. It was forcing me to realise that we were definitely on the downward slope with our diagnosis of advanced Alzheimer's, and I felt very emotional about it. It's one thing to know where you are going and quite another to see the massive changes in your loved one confirmed by professionals and admitting that you need help.

I look back with thanks that we were in Cornwall at the start of this phase of needing help, as, right from the start; it was obvious that not all support groups are the same. I thank our lucky stars that we were able to join the memory café in Lanivet as it was excellent and run by caring, committed people and volunteers that really could not do enough for people with dementia and their carers.

I found Graham's first visit to the memory café nerve-racking, as I was not sure that he would take to the groups initially. The first time I dropped him off, I experienced the same feeling I had when dropping my children off at playgroup.

Was he going to like it? Would he mix and join in? Would he want to come home?

Waiting with the other family members and carers at pick-up time, I was struck again at the similarity to young children as we were all waiting to see if smiles were the order of the day or anger and resentment.

There is a saying, isn't there? 'Nothing much between the cradle and the grave, except a s***, shower and a shave.' I can resonate with that!

Graham came out of the memory café beaming from ear-to-ear and I heaved a huge sigh of relief as he had clearly had a fabulous time.

It was wonderful to see my magic man smile again.

From Graham's point of view, what was there not to like? People, cake and tea. It was a winning combination.

From that first meeting at the 'All for One Community Centre' in Lanivet, our world got a little easier.

Graham enjoyed all the activities available there. A favourite was the men-only group of indoor bowls which he loved and, much to my surprise; he was suddenly interested in joining a newly formed dementia choir also in Lanivet.

Graham had always enjoyed the company of men from when he played football back in the day and subsequently golf. I tried very hard to keep the golf going for him but, having lost his ability to converse with others easily and to keep check of the number of holes played, the fun went out of it for him and he stopped playing. I bought a little counting tool for him to use but the joy had gone out of the game for him and, when Graham made the decision not to play golf anymore, he missed the camaraderie that being amongst men brought him.

I also then became the sole stimulus for him which, I do not mind admitting, was hard work.

Indoor bowls with fellow dementia patients became a wonderful replacement for golf as it was the company he enjoyed rather than the sport, in those years of being able to join in with others and brought the fun and banter back into his life.

Graham is well-known for being tone-deaf but he surprised us all by developing a new love of music and singing. We were lucky enough to have within the village a newly-formed choir for people with dementia.

He loved the choir. I cannot express how much difference singing with others made to Graham. Being part of a choir (run by an amazing woman called Maureen and her pianist, Beryl) gave him something very special. It was a lovely moment when the memory choir and the local primary school all gathered together for a Christmas carol service at Lanivet Church. The old and the young all together was very poignant and meaningful.

What these groups provided was very important to Graham's well-being as he had peer support and memory support twice a week and, every third week, the memory café was available.

It was a fantastic service and the people who run it were inspirational to know. I really cannot recommend these groups highly enough. Even if you think your loved one will not love it, please try the groups as your loved one is not the same as they once were; everything has changed, and this might have changed for them.

If your person with dementia doesn't initially like the idea of groups, I would think back to my remark about toddlers; encourage them to go, stay yourself if you need to initially and you might be surprised and, more importantly, your loved one with dementia might be surprised how much they enjoy it.

The other wonderful thing that Gerard introduced us to was a local charity called Purple Angels. The charity was created by dementia patient Norman McNamara and part of what they do is provide free MP3 players with fifteen preloaded tracks of the patient's choice to use at home. The MP3 was a godsend as Graham could escape into his own world once the headphones were on and he was in his special place. Brilliant idea!

It was at this time that Graham developed an obsession with colouring. One of the mental health team, Sue, suggested it to me and was met with a blank look at the time, as Graham had never expressed any interest in colouring. However, as things became more difficult, I bought a colouring book with mandalas for Graham to colour in. Graham loved it and spent literally hours painstakingly colouring in the mandalas each day.

I learnt an important lesson that day and that was, just because Graham did not like something in the past, did not mean he would not like it now; everything was worth a try to keep the magic man contented and happy.

Part of the keeping a smile on Graham's face campaign, led me to get a second-hand guitar for Graham to strum along to music with. He loved it for a while and I have happy moments to look back on of this stage of dementia.

It was now becoming obvious that we needed to try to sell our home again, as Graham's needs had increased so much and I knew that worse was to come. On the second attempt, we did sell but the home we found in Suffolk pulled out of the sale just as lockdown hit the following year March 2020 and we lost the sale. It worked out for the best in the end as, if we had moved at that time, I would not have been able to keep Graham at home for as long as I did. Life works in mysterious ways, doesn't it?

It was definitely a hidden blessing.

With no move being possible, due to Covid for the immediate future, meant we had to dig in metaphorically and physically.

Graham had passed another of my lines in the sand by now and was urinary incontinent so pads were a way of life.

Lines in the sand are useful but, in my experience, you step over them when you reach them and, my next line in the sand of bowel incontinence, had thankfully not been reached. I really did not feel I would be able to cope with that aspect of incontinence and pushed the thought aside, hoping it would never happen.

What was slowly wearing me out were the nights. After a long day when you are dog-tired, you then must get up to change pads several times a night due to nocturnal wanderings and Graham's habit of taking the pads off as soon as I left the bedroom. Looking back at some of those times, our life was like a comedy farce except, of course, it was not funny at four in the morning. I would walk into Graham's room and literally paddle to the bed. Thankfully, laminate flooring helped save the house from the worst of it but, it really was difficult, and mopping up the sea of urine at four in the morning tests your love for your husband, I can tell you.

As your loved one becomes nocturnal, you just cannot do the day as well as the night and stay sane. Should Graham now be in a home? Everything about the thought made me scream 'no!'

However, I was beginning to realise that I was struggling to keep Graham safe at home. He was wandering out of the house and down the lanes during the day and, nocturnal wandering at night, meant I could not keep him out of the kitchen where many dangers lay in wait for him, along with several steps on the ground floor of the house. I also felt, (because I was tired, no doubt) that I just wasn't giving him what he needed which then made me doubt the route I had chosen to keep him at home at this time.

Because of the medications Graham was taking, he was also at high risk of falls. We were an accident waiting to happen.

I requested a Continuing Health Care Assessment and a Carers Assessment at this time.

I do not believe that dementia should be classified as a 'social care issue' as it currently is, and the NHS is doing us a great disservice by describing it this way. Depriving the most vulnerable families' access to little or no funding unless your savings or assets are under £23k is a scandal. From my experience of having walked the cancer journey path and now the dementia path, I can personally say that the stresses and strains are the same on both pathways as both illnesses affect physical, emotional and mental well-being and absolutely should be supported by the Continuing Health Care purse. When I have time, I am going to bang loudly on the drum about this lack of equality in healthcare; it is just not good enough and it is essentially a cost-cutting exercise by the NHS not to pay anything towards care for dementia patients. It is a disgrace.

You do develop the darkest sense of humour to cope, and I did laugh on many occasions. Two occasions that stick in my mind are when Graham set the fall alarm off by thrashing around at night and I was woken by the alarm sounding and a male voice saying, "don't worry, Mr King, the paramedics are on their way," through the loudspeaker! I moved downstairs very fast on that occasion to cancel the alarm. Another time, after the third pad change, I was jolted awake by Graham shouting, "staff, staff" at the bottom of the stairs for the fourth change which he had helpfully started himself!

This lack of sleep led me to put a first toe in the water with a carer, as I could not yet contemplate putting Graham into a home.

Things that helped and stimulated during this stage;

- Music, either in the room to sing along to or on MP3 player and headphones via Purple Angel Charity.
- Playing drums, saucepans or strumming second-hand guitar.
- Colouring, we choose mandalas as Graham was interested in them, so choose something your person will like.
- Indoor carpet bowls.
- Exercise bike.
- Jenga.

- Connect Four.
- Choir.
- Memory café.
- Singing at home.
- Meditation.
- Talking wristwatch to be able to tell the time.

Chapter 8

DIFFICULT TIMES

The first attempt at having someone to help was not a great success. I met a woman needing accommodation and who had experience as a carer. It didn't work out on either side for several reasons and, after a few months, Graham's needs outstripped the time she could offer us but it gave me a good idea of what Graham needed going forward.

Desperation is the enemy of discernment. By this, I mean that you may accept almost anybody into your life in the quest to make life a little better. This may well apply to friendships you make at this time. Please try not to make the same mistake I did; having no one in your life is better than the wrong person, whether that be a carer or a friend.

Nevertheless, please do not be too hard on yourself if you do make less than great decisions at this time. You are doing your best and your best is good enough.

People come into your life for a reason, a season or a lifetime and, in this period, I understood this better than ever before in my life.

I learnt something about myself during this period and that was that I could not cope with aggression. I had not really realised this before, but Graham's paranoia and aggression had now become constant companions and I was triggered back to those bad old days of my adolescence.

Aggression, I now know, is my personal tipping point.

When you are frightened, life becomes much more difficult. Every time aggression happened, usually every day when the postman arrived, Graham kicked off.

I would freeze as I was taken back to my teens when I had been pushed into a corner and hit by my father for having an opinion different to his. Graham was inadvertently now triggering that fear locked within me.

I made a plan to put the post-box elsewhere on the property, but the post still had to come into the house, I couldn't always hide it in time, and off we went again...

During these episodes of aggression, Graham started to walk out of the house and out onto the country lanes. I realised he was trying to make his way to Lanivet some three miles away to go to the clubs. The first few times it happened; he would come back with me once he had reached the end of the lane; if I was lucky enough to realise he had gone out.

After the first few attempts at walking to Lanivet, Graham got wise to my diverting him and refused to get in the car with me. He would give me a little smirk and carry on walking. Not great for my blood pressure or my patience!

This was potentially a huge problem, as the busy A30 ran right next to the road he was walking along, and we had a few farcical moments when I tried to block the lane with our car in order to make him turn around but he just attempted to climb over the bonnet of the car.

I've learnt a great deal of patience since these things happened but, at the time,, I was less so and I would try to speak gently through gritted teeth and a fake sunny smile saying, "let's get in the car, shall we, Graham?"... unsurprisingly, he didn't want to!

I quickly realised that, as Graham no longer knew who I was, it was obvious that, when I opened the mail or asked him to get in the car with me, it triggered his paranoia. Who was this strange woman taking control of his life?

I know I will not be alone in feeling the fear of living in a confined space with a dearly loved husband who I no longer wanted to turn my back on. In my case, this was because I felt very unsafe, as Graham is a powerfully built man.

My lovely neighbour, Clare, gave me a 'safe word' to text if things got out of hand, it was 'cauliflower!' Yes, cauliflower, only a farmer's wife would think of that one!

It was at this point that I accepted things were getting out of hand and I acknowledged I did need help, so I rang the mental health team and said I needed support.

One advantage of being seen as someone who is coping is, when you do ask for support, people know it must be bad for you to seek help and they then react quickly.

The out-of-hours mental health team were brilliant and came within hours after realising how very unwell Graham was after speaking to him on his mobile. They told me he was very mentally unstable and, as a first action, they gave sedatives to calm the whole situation down.

The team were helpful and, after a meeting to discuss Graham's case, they prescribed anti-psychotic medication. For several months, the medication worked really well and, for a short while, it gave me back my happy-go-lucky husband.

All medicine comes with side effects, of course, but it's a matter of balancing the benefits against the risks and, looking at photographs of Graham from that time, I have no doubt that Graham was able to enjoy his life once again with the right medication. In this case, the prescribed medication was Risperidone along with an antidepressant.

Graham and I had talked in the past about his mum having Alzheimer's and the difficulties his father had undergone caring for her at home. We agreed that if either of us reached a point where we did not know the other, then we would want to be put in a home.

However, when reality strikes, it is not so easy to make that decision. I wasn't ready to consider a residential home for Graham and he (aside from his paranoia and aggression) seemed happy at home so I made the decision that, if I could raise the funds, I would prefer Graham stayed in our own home for as long as possible, ideally until he passed into spirit.

We were introduced to a special woman called Kelly who quickly became Graham's 'fun time' companion. Kelly was pretty, blond and loved Graham so, of course, they bonded well together. They toured around Cornwall going to all the best places for afternoon tea and lunch whilst I got on with our charity work and the remaining holiday let.

Kelly was a diamond. Cheerful, chatty and quick on her feet, absolutely manna from heaven to us both, she became a close friend to me and a fabulous partner-in-crime to Graham.

Life gradually became more intense over that year as Graham's needs grew until Kelly was visiting us for fifteen hours a week. I needed this amount of help to keep my head above water but, with the support from the groups and Kelly, I was just about managing.

Kelly introduced us to the delights of 'Alexa.' Alexa, as you will probably know, is an amazing piece of artificial intelligence. Alexa has many skills but, for us she acted as a music machine and we had music readily available day and night of any genre. It was possible to change Graham's mood in an instant by choosing the right music from a previous happy occasion. We danced around the kitchen, sang along and giggled like children with the joy of having unlimited music in our lives.

COVID

We, along with so many others, were left isolated and seemingly abandoned in our homes when the country locked down. Explaining to Graham why he could no longer leave the house and mix with his dementia club friends was beyond his comprehension. His only way of coping was to see me as the person who was stopping him from doing all of these things.

It was a terrible time as Graham's reaction to confinement at home was further paranoia and aggression. There is no reasoning with dementia and he could not be swayed from his view that I alone was the culprit, and was standing in the way of his happiness.

Doing the first six months of Covid restrictions, it was very, very difficult to do anything other than survive. The separation from others with the same condition and the complete lack of interaction from the groups devastated Graham's mental well-being and the decline in his condition was rapid, profound and irreversible.

Dementia is often referred to as a very cruel disease but I do not see it that way. I actually think it is a kindness when the person with dementia reaches a stage where they no longer remember how life was before the dementia began as their anxiety reduces. Whilst the confusion looks worse from the outside, it does not seem to bother the patient quite as much as it bothers everyone else.

Graham's increasing dementia also meant that he was spared the great grief of having to deal with the loss of his beloved dog, Madge. Madge was a beautiful sprocker. I used to joke they were unnaturally close, and she was the other woman in our marriage, consequently, I worried a lot about what would happen if Madge got ill. She had a habit of growing tumours and, so far, they had been benign but then, as if life was not challenging enough, Madge developed a fast-growing aggressive malignant tumour in her jaw. It was growing at an alarming rate and the vet and I decided an operation would be of little benefit to Madge and would only prolong her discomfort.

Eventually, I could put the decision off no longer and I had to make the heart-breaking decision to have her put to sleep. Graham could not make that decision for her so I had to do it. It is a hard and lonely place to be the spouse of a dementia patient at times like this.

It was a very low moment in my life when the dreadful day came and I drove down to the vet by myself with Madge sitting on the seat beside me. Due to Covid restrictions, I sat with her in the boot of the car to enable her to be sedated before she was carried into the vet. Whilst she dozed off to sleep, I talked to her about how we would all be together again one day and kissed her goodbye.

Once she was asleep and snoring peacefully, I then handed her over and waited for her carefully wrapped body to be brought back to me.

My heart broke.

I took Madge home and was greeted by Alice, our little Jack Russell terrier, and Kelly, who had been looking after Graham. Graham and I sat late into the afternoon cuddling Madge's body on the settee with Alice until it was time to bury her in the garden. Graham was tearful but managed the situation well and I was thankful that the dementia stopped him from feeling things as deeply as he once would have done.

The heavens opened as I dug a large hole in the flowerbed for Madge. Graham stood by, silently watching me and I was glad at least that he was not (as far as I could tell) feeling the colossal grief that I was feeling.

That was a very bad day indeed as, normally, we would have been able to comfort each other but, now, I was on my own with my thoughts and the rain as I carefully placed Madge in the hole and covered her up with earth.

Madge was never spoken about by Graham after that and I thought that dementia on this occasion had been kind to him as he was distanced emotionally from the loss of the dog he had adored for eight years.

There were some new changes for Graham during this time, such as feeling fear when away from home. As we drove along the Cornish lanes, Graham became increasingly agitated and hated going out on trips. It was not his fault, of course, but it became clear that, if I wanted to carry on with any kind of life, I would have to learn to begin to do more things by myself.

This was a painful stage in the process of acceptance; letting go of what we once had, as we had always lived our lives so closely together.

Sometimes, the grief of what we had lost was overwhelming for me and, at other times, I could bravely peek at a future without Graham in it. This brought on many tears and Kelly was a wonderfully comforting presence during my bleak times.

I do not know about you but I hate crying. I never find it useful, it just makes me feel worse and I have an irritating habit that, when I start crying, I find it difficult to stop. I know I am just crying for all the things that I have felt grief about throughout my life but I do not find it helpful. Another person will say they feel better after a good cry. Not me; I feel ten times worse!

So, cry if it helps but, otherwise, as a great friend of mine once said, "Kick on, Angie, Kick on."

Thank heavens for people like Kelly, as Covid had brought us to our knees mentally, emotionally and physically. With her boundless enthusiasm and zest for life, she infected Graham and me with a we-can-do-this-together attitude.

The memory café and all the groups remained closed with no hope of reopening in the near future and the effect on Graham's well-being continued to be devastating. We were allocated a visit once a week from Jess (one of the memory team staff) and she came out to visit us at home and sang with Graham.

When Jess could no longer come to visit us at home, Maureen from the memory choir offered to call Graham on the phone once a week and sing with Graham. He really enjoyed doing this but the decline in his cognitive abilities continued partly because of isolation and partly, of course, as a progression of the disease. Eventually, there came a time when he could no longer follow the words, or the tune and the calls began to agitate and confuse him, so we had to stop. Maureen and others were real stars and did their absolute best to help us under very difficult circumstances.

Things that helped during lockdown;

- The right medication from the Mental Health Team.
- Music via Alexa and MP3 player from the charity Purple Angels.
- Kelly, companion/carer.
- Beki, carer for personal care when needed.
- Fall alarm.
- Police when Graham went walkabout.
- Gardening.

NB: Any household or gardening job can be adapted to be shared together.

Graham was so much happier if he felt useful in some way.

Chapter 9

MOVING HOME

We had a new person enter our life at this time, a lodger had moved into the Sunflower Lodge to help me pay for care.

Sam, our lodger, became a very good friend during the time she lived at the lodge, baking cakes for us and generally sprinkling her special magic liberally over our lives. Graham was very fond of her, as was I, and she made me hoot with laughter as she regaled us with her adventurous life, far removed from the life we were currently living. She was great fun to have around.

During Sam's time with us, I managed to sell the Sunflower Lodge, which was a huge relief as, even with Kelly coming fifteen hours a week, being awake most nights with Graham was slowly but surely sucking the energy out of me, making it difficult to cope during the day. Now, at last, I had some funds to enable me to go ahead and advertise for a live-in carer.

One lovely carer who sounded perfect was stuck in South Africa due to lockdown and another who did accept the post, travelled to Cornwall for a trial period and then left within two days.

I had made it very clear that Graham was well advanced in his dementia journey but, when she turned up, it was apparent that she had not really listened to my description of the work involved as, bless her, with her dodgy hips and mobility, it was obvious that she needed more care than Graham did. I think she imagined she would sit quietly beside him whilst she knitted as a companion! Very far from the truth.

It was a bit of a blow as I now had a wake-up call that, even with money, the right carer is hard to find.

Things were tough, very tough now, mainly due to the massive decline in Graham's dementia, worsened by isolation. When I am stuck, I ask for help from those upstairs. 'Upstairs' for me is my loved ones who are in spirit. Having asked for their help, help did come. A local carer called Beki, who said she could not live in, but could come three times a day five days a week, contacted me.

Err, yes, please!

Beki took care of Graham's increasing need for personal care mornings and evening, and a couple of hours' midday, three days a week for social interaction; it was brilliant to have her support alongside Kelly and it really took the pressure off me.

I was now in a much better place and, between Kelly, Beki and myself, I was able to manage.

Despite everything, we had some very good and happy times together and named ourselves Graham's angels. Magic man was happy again.

Christmas 2020 was our last Christmas in Cornwall, and it was one of big emotional milestones.

My advice is, don't look back at what you've lost otherwise you are performing an act of self-torture. Just accept where you're at and try to be present in the moment; it's easier that way.

I had plenty of time to reflect on our lives and consider where we were going during the strange time between Christmas and New Year. I began to see clearly that Cornwall was not a place that I wanted to be a widow in as I was very much alone, despite having one good set of neighbours. We had chosen our isolated home when it was the two of us but, now there was only me, it was not the best place to be.

We had tried to move back to Suffolk before, as you know, but our house did not sell on the first attempt and, on the second attempt, we were scuppered by Covid.

After much thought, I decided that it was going to be third time lucky to sell and that the time was right to move back to our circle of friends in Suffolk. I was under no illusion that they could help in a practical way anymore than my neighbours could in Cornwall, but they would be there for me in an emotional sense for what was to come in the future.

Moving with a loved one who has advanced Alzheimer's is not for the faint-hearted but, then again, I am not faint-hearted and, so, I went ahead and put the house on the market.

Offers came rushing in as the market was hot, very hot, as so many people wanted to get out of living in a city due to Covid. Also, as a special gift to us, as a result of the high demand this time, our house was valued far above what it had been the previous year with the added bonus that there were a number of people bidding above the asking price for it.

We sold very quickly with me carrying out all the viewings due to Covid restrictions. Conducting the viewings was quite a challenge, with Graham not quite understanding why so many people wanted to see around our house. I had told him that we were moving but he did not retain the information and, so, each time someone came to view, I told him that the viewers were friends who had come along to see how lovely our home was before we moved back to Suffolk.

Graham accepted this explanation happily.

Unfortunately, the market was identical in Suffolk (hot) and each house I saw online was quickly sold before I could even view it. People, it seemed, wanted to live in rural locations and live a different lifestyle.

It was going to prove to be very difficult to move as none of the houses I could afford in Suffolk had a downstairs bedroom and shower room, which Graham now needed.

With all this going on in the background and Graham continuing to get steadily worse—not sleeping at night, unsteady on his feet, relentless decline in cognition due to isolation from the outside world—it was a pretty challenging time.

I was beginning to lose hope of finding somewhere to buy when a friend rang me from Suffolk and told me about a well-thought-of residential home in Lowestoft that was meant to be the best in its field for group and social activities for people with dementia.

I already knew that Graham would need to be in respite whilst I moved us to Suffolk so I rang the home and it was agreed that he would go and stay there whilst I moved and, if he liked it, he could become a resident.

Considering a residential home for Graham had only become a real possibility because we had sold the house. This is the state of social care today; if I wanted to have Graham in care, I would have to fund it myself as a self-funder. When I hear people say, no one has to sell their homes to provide care, I smile ruefully as that is exactly what I did to be able to provide care for Graham.

Graham was pleased with the idea of a care home, his mum had stayed in one and he had been a regular visitor. I hoped that he would be happier and safer than I could keep him at home. He would be part of a group again and he loved clubs so I was optimistic that I was doing the right thing for Graham. The next week was spent washing clothes, ironing on nametags and packing his bags to take him up to Lowestoft. In the evening, before we were to leave, he hugged me and thanked me for arranging it for him. It was a low moment for me but a good moment for Graham.

Little did either of us know what was ahead of us.

Beki heroically offered to make the seven-hour drive with me, and I gratefully accepted. I did not want to take Kelly, as I knew we would not be able to hide our emotions from each other and, if we got upset, it would confuse Graham.

As if as a sign that I was making the right choice, the evening before we left, Graham lost some of the strength in his legs and I really struggled to get him off the loo, which made me feel I was making the right decision.

I had a sense the place had come up in the home just in time, as soon I would not have been able to manage Graham's needs at home, so it was with some relief that we set off on the long drive to Lowestoft.

We stopped at the first service station on the M4 and had a MacDonald's together before setting off again. We did rather well consider the distance, until we hit the Orwell Bridge in Suffolk where a huge traffic jam was blocking all traffic in many directions around Ipswich.

Graham was now agitated and hit his head with his hand in pure frustration as he needed a pad change but we could not get out of the traffic to be able to help him.

I am surprised the top of my head did not blow off with the pressure of it!

We finally arrived at the home at seven-thirty p.m., having left Cornwall twelve hours earlier.

Having arrived, we were all tested for Covid and then Graham got out of the car and looked up at the building, he said it looked very nice. So far so good, I thought.

Finally, we went through the doors and were shown up to Graham's new room. It was lovely and we quickly unpacked and made it a little more like home for him before going for a tour around the home.

Graham had assumed magic showman mode as we toured around and, as we went into the dining room, a group of women looked up at him with a glint in their eyes, as he said with all his usual charm, "Hello, ladies"! Faces lit up in the room and I felt it was going to be okay.

We then made our planned quick exit to allow Graham to settle in. I will never forget his confused face at the window beckoning me to come back in.

My world officially fell apart.

It's one thing to feel it must be done and quite another to actually leave your loved one in a place that you really are not able to explain why and when it will end.

It was heart-breaking.

Beki and I stayed at the Premier Inn nearby to rest before driving straight back to Cornwall the next day.

Thank God for Beki as she drove most of the way home and, from time-to-time, instructed me to stop snivelling! Just what I needed; as sympathy would have been no good at all.

It was an easy drive back to Cornwall and, as I walked into my now-empty house, I just wanted to shut up shop and lick my wounds.

I had not factored in my lodger, Sam, who turned up with a bottle of wine, which we promptly drank and got very tipsy. There was a hilarious moment when I realised it was bin day the next morning so we staggered up the drive with the bins, giggling loudly, wondering what the neighbours would be thinking of us.

The consumed wine made that evening bearable and, the next day, the hunt began in earnest to find a house in Suffolk as quickly as I could. I was now seven hours from Graham and I knew I would not be able to cope with that for very long.

There was so little to choose from in Suffolk in the area we wanted to live, so I took virtual tours on WhatsApp with the estate agents. A gut-feeling prompted me to make an offer on a cottage that I saw in this way and I arranged to see it in person a week before I moved in.

It was a small, thatched grade two-listed cottage. Did I want it? Absolutely not. I had an idea of an open-plan barn that I could bring Graham home to if he didn't settle at the residential home, but desperate times call for desperate measures.

There was something about the cottage that made me feel it would be the right one for now. Mad, I know, but, as I said earlier, desperation is the enemy of discernment!

Our buyers in Cornwall wanted to complete before the end of stamp duty and the pressure was on to get going; the cottage was available so the date was set to move home on the 30th June 2021.

It was now all-hands-on-deck as I had a lot of furniture to get rid of from the two holiday lets and our home and downsizing became the order of the day. The cottage I was buying was cute but it was small, very small, so it was time to be ruthless. I gave many things away to good friends and, when the day of the move came, I was ready to fit into Lilycot or so I thought.

I used the same removal people that were bringing my buyers down to Cornwall, as it seemed to make sense to do so. Never again! They were truly the removal company from hell and tried to ram my house contents into three transit vans. The removal man had carried out a WhatsApp tour of my contents in Cornwall but he had hopelessly misjudged it. On the day of the move, after arriving four hours later than planned, his main priority was to get back to Christchurch to watch the England match and not to do a good job for me. As they came down the drive, I had a feeling of impending doom when I saw the three transit vans but knew it was too late to turn back now.

I was getting quite good at making the best of things, but these people pushed me to the limit when they arrived four hours later than planned and then arrived to offload in Suffolk four hours late at two p.m. the following afternoon instead of ten a.m.

When the doors on the vans opened in Suffolk, it looked for the entire world as if the contents had been thrown on board and then the door had been slammed shut to keep it all in. Horrendous!

After offloading and pushing boxes and furniture into every square inch, the 'boss' walked off-site at five p.m. to get home for a beer, leaving me with all the boxes and furniture piled up on every available floor space.

Naturally, I complained, to be greeted by a load of sexual discrimination. I will never use a company from the Trust-a-Trader website again. The company I used really needed to be on Rogue Traders.

I did thank God Graham wasn't sitting in the middle of the chaos as it would have been the only thing that could have possibly made things worse.

I am fortunate to have friends who rang around to try to get me some help and, a few hours later, a stranger turned up at the door to help me clear a path through the boxes so that I could at least make a bed for the night for the dogs and myself.

Angels really do arrive when you need them most.

Nothing I can offer in the way of advice for this chapter, other than to say that, whatever happens, you will be able to cope and go on to survive.

Honestly, you will.

Chapter 10

SAFE OR NOT SAFE?

Our new home was small and beautiful. A chocolate box-type cottage that I had not planned on, but it was the only thing available to me in the crazy world of stamp duty deadlines. I only bought it because I thought Graham was happy and being looked after in his care home and, therefore, it did not matter if it were too small for both of us as it would just be me. Realistically, I had come to the end of what I thought I could do by myself at home anyway and, as nothing had changed, I had no plans to bring Graham home.

I was soon to learn that what I had hoped for from the care home (to keep Graham safe and well-cared-for) was not what Graham was experiencing.

I was horrified when I went to see Graham the first day after I moved to Suffolk to see him lying like a palliative care patient in his room with large friction sores on his heels, swollen legs and running a very high temperature with a very obvious urine infection.

My heart crashed into my boots and I asked to speak to the manager.

In the NHS, we used to call this type of chat "a shit sandwich," that is, say something nice then say what you really have to say and then end with something nice.

As I could not make contact directly with the manager, who was off-site, an email would have to do.

This then was the first email after being told the manager was away at present.

'Dear Manager,

First, may I say how impressed I was initially at the care my husband, Graham, received in the first month within your care home. It was clear from the Facebook videos, that your staff and especially the activities team could not have worked harder to make Graham feel at home.

However, since that first month and following my first visit to the home a month ago, I have spoken to your senior carer twice with concerns that Graham's risperidone dose is too high. He is clearly ('knocked off') sleeping all day which is having a detrimental effect on his physical and mental well-being.

As you know, I have been looking after Graham alone at home for some years and have liaised closely with the mental health teams in Cornwall. Despite being a large, strong man, Graham is very sensitive to medication and, on his admission to your care, he was on a prescribed dose of ½ mg of risperidone twice a day.

I am unsure why the doctor has increased his dose to 1 mg twice a day and why I was not told about the increase. I would like to understand what symptoms the GP thinks they are treating by increasing the dose, as it is clearly knocking him off his feet, which has resulted in swollen legs and an inability to stand, or walk; his quality of life has diminished because of this.

I would like, as a matter of urgency, a review of his medication and his care.

As you know, I am now living in Suffolk so I am happy to come up to any multi-discipline meetings about Graham if this would be helpful to you and your team, and I would appreciate you informing me of any changes in medication as soon as they are made both now and in the future.

I do understand about the progression of the disease and the effects of medication having worked in the NHS within cancer and dementia care for many years and, all that matters to me, is that Graham has 'bespoke medication' relevant to him and not a blanket medical cosh.

I am sure you will agree that person-centred care is important, no matter how little cognitive function is left, for our loved ones.

I look forward to hearing from you with your views on the best way forward for Graham and I would be grateful if you can respond to my email once you have had a chance to discuss my comments.

Once again, thank you for caring for Graham so well initially and I do appreciate you have his best interests at heart but, it is clear from his rapid decline, that his needs are not being met.'

I did not get a response for almost a week and, in the meantime, Graham developed a high temperature that was not picked up because the thermometer the staff were using on patients was giving a false low reading. I know that the staff were doing their best but, anyone with any caring skills, could see that he had a high temperature despite what the thermometer read.

I was gutted to have to consider that I had placed him in their care and they had taken him from a walking-well-state of being, to flat-on-his-back looking like a palliative care patient in two months.

Sometimes I feel like my whole life has been a series of fights; fighting for people who cannot fight for themselves. Once again, I had to take on a system that I had trusted who were letting Graham down.

I was now being asked to fight again, battle weary from placing Graham in the home, from the move, from the terrible removal company and the stress of finding somewhere to live, it seemed I had no choice but to straighten my shoulders and fight again.

I visited Graham the next day to ensure I was with him when the GP came for his scheduled visit. The GP was due to arrive at three p.m. and turned up at six-thirty p.m. He took one look at Graham and said he had a high temperature and an infection, ordered a urine dip and some antibiotics and then set off on his rounds again.

I left the home that evening feeling that Graham was going to be being looked after properly because the dip test would be done and his medication would start to bring whatever was causing the infection under control—wrong again.

When I arrived to visit two days later, his urine had still not been tested, blood tests had not been carried out and he was not getting any better.

Now, I was mad, very mad.

Stronger communication was obviously called for.

'Dear Manager,

I have sent emails and WhatsApp messages about my husband, Graham King's care over the past week and have asked twice for a member of the management team to contact me, all to no avail.

Graham was admitted into your care on the 17th of May, he has advanced dementia but was cognitive in his own way and was able to walk around well.

Now, two months later, due to lack of care and vigilance by your facility and neglect of his physical needs, he is a shell of the man who was admitted to you.

a) It began with cellulitis a week after he joined you and has been a downward spiral since then on a physical level.
b) Since my move to Suffolk a week ago, I have been aghast at the last of basic care that I have witnessed for Graham within your facility.
c) A month ago on my first visit, I noticed that Graham was very sleepy and that he had a huge blister on the heel of his left foot. It is no surprise that this meant he could not weight bear. Why this

friction from the bedsheets has this not been noticed and proactive treatment taken?

d) His medication had been increased for 'agitation' but -one had informed me, despite me holding POA and this led to his being 'knocked off' during the day, resulting in more inactivity.
e) Then the gout set in and two visits to A&E followed in one week; one for a hugely swollen knee when 70 ml of fluid was drained off, a diagnosis of gout, and another A&E visit as staff were not able to rouse Graham in the morning.
f) Why did no one suspect overmedication? Why has the gout not been acted on since, he clearly still has it in his left inflamed swollen foot and his elbow joint on the left side and possibly in his right knee.
g) This lack of vigilance has resulted in physical pain for Graham which, due to lack of care, was just being ignored apart from a dose of paracetamol—anyone with an awareness of gout will know that paracetamol is ineffective for gout and a suitable painkiller prescribed by a doctor was needed.
h) Last Sunday when I visited, it was clear that Graham was over-medicated and in pain. This is unforgivable and staff rightly asked for a GP to visit him on the Monday at three p.m. I came up to the home to be present when the GP came and was alarmed to see that Graham clearly had a temperature but had cold peripherals along with

delirium, making me feel he was very sick. The care assistant had done her best and used the in-house temperature gauge to take Graham's temperature, which showed 36.3°, as did my reading and indeed hers.

i) I waited three-and-a-half hours for the doctor to come (the GP had not prioritized Graham as he was not told Graham had a temperature but, of course, we now know he did). During this time, it became obvious to me that Graham had a urine infection, as the odour from his wet pad was very strong. When the GP arrived, his temperature gauge gave a reading of 38.5° and the GP ordered a full review of his bloods to try to establish what the root cause was and asked why a dip test of his urine had not been carried out. The GP instructed the care staff to take a urine sample the next morning, as it was "too late that day to take one as you only do them in the mornings." He also prescribed antibiotics, which the following day the nurse changed to liquid form to enable the carers to administer it.

Two days later;

1) No urine test has been done and no blood test has been carried out, despite me hearing very clearly the GP ordering a "full set of bloods." This lack of joined-up care seems to be down to lack of communication in your care teams with the excuse that they have been very busy; too busy to stop my

husband suffering in pain that was wholly avoidable… I am shocked at this basic lack of carer skills.

2) These are serious lack of care issues and, if I receive no reply on this third occasion of writing to you, I will go the next step up if I must. Please let me be clear, I have the highest regard for your emotional and activities staff along with the care staff that I have met, BUT Graham is being let down badly by you.
3) My only priority is to protect and care for Graham and I had hoped that I had found the right partner in your care facility to share the journey with. Sadly, this is not the case so far.

   I want Graham to stay with you as he is now settled but, if these serious matters cannot be addressed, he is certainly not getting the care he deserves, and I would like a full plan of how you will ensure this does not happen to Graham or any other patient in your care again.'

This email did get the following response and I was invited in to discuss my concerns the following week.

'Hi Angie

Just to update you, a sample has been taken over this morning, we had dip-tested it last night and contacted the surgery first thing with our findings, we eventually got a fresh sample to be sent off today. Surgery confirmed that the antibiotics he started on Tuesday should help.

I am looking into all your concerns and, as indicated last night, will action anything where necessary; we have had an emergency senior team meeting to discuss Graham and the home, and are making changes with immediate effect to give assurances and comfort to you, moving forward. We are now working on an active care plan so you can be assured of expectations in regards to all areas of Graham's that will assist others too and I shall contact you first thing tomorrow to arrange to meet.

Once again, I am so sorry you had to email three times before getting a response and can assure you that this will never happen again.

Kind regards'

When I arrived for our planned meeting the following week, I was met at the door by the manager to be told the home was not allowing any visitors due to two care assistants having tested positive for Covid.

I was assured that, when the home opened again, I would be invited to develop a care plan with the manager and that she would ask a Continuing Healthcare Assessment to take place.

Neither of these things ever happened and my request to be registered as Graham's essential caregiver which would have allowed me to support Graham even if the home was closed was never responded to.

NB: every care home resident can choose to nominate an essential caregiver who may visit the home to attend to essential care needs. The essential caregiver should be enabled to visit in all circumstances, including if the care home is in outbreak (but not if the essential caregiver or resident are COVID-positive.)

The home being shut to visitors meant that Graham was trapped inside a home that I no longer had confidence in.

Faced with lack of access, there was nothing more I could do, so I just had to wait until the home opened again in ten days' time.

Graham was a very changed man by the time I next saw him, and we hugged for a long time when we eventually were able to spend time together.

Now, that I was able to visit Graham regularly again, we were able to enjoy some golden moments together especially when Graham was fit enough to get in the car. Two favourite trips were to the seafront at Gorleston near Yarmouth and to Lowestoft, where we parked in front of the pier and ate hot doughnuts and ice cream washed down with a bag of chips and a cup of tea.

It was lovely to be able to visit regularly again but I would often arrive to find Graham unshaven, unwashed and with a wet pad on. Having worked in care, I was well aware of the challenges they were working with but, for heaven's sake, this was allegedly one of the best homes in the county and basic personal care was not being carried out even when they knew I was coming in to visit.

I was told that Graham was challenging and aggressive to some staff and I knew he could be, so I accepted they might be right and recognised that this might be behind his unwashed appearance on some occasions.

However, when Graham had three falls in one month, I knew I had to consider changing the home to one where I could help with personal care and be able to provide the extra pair of hands that I hoped would make the difference to Graham's quality of life. If Graham was nearby, I rationalised that it would make it possible for me to go in every day and do the personal care and, that way, Graham would get what he needed and I could fill in the gaps in care.

My advice;

- You are going to have to advocate for your loved ones when care is substandard.
- It happens often and you need to be strong and report the facility to the safeguarding team if necessary.
- Your loved one needs your love but they also need you to stand up for them when required as they cannot do so for themselves.

Chapter 11

TIME TO BE BRAVE

It was the care home's refusal to discuss my being registered as Graham's essential caregiver (ECG) that made me lose trust in the home that Graham was in. Not allowing me in as an ECG said to me (rightly or wrongly) that there were things they did not want me to see within the home. The manager had already closed the home for three weeks due to a Covid case amongst the staff and I could see that, with the winter coming up ahead of us, this would be a regular occurrence. If I were an ECG, I would be able to go in and see Graham even when closed for Covid, without it, I could not.

This being the case, Graham had to come out of there.

In preparation for the move, I visited a nursing home and a care home close to our new home, thinking that I could then visit much more regularly and Graham's quality of life would improve. I sought reassurance from the managers at the potential new homes that I could become Graham's registered ECG and they happily agreed that I could. This helped me make the decision to move Graham from one home to another in Knodishall, a five-minute drive from our new home.

If the home had agreed my ECG status, I would have elected to leave Graham where he was settled to avoid any disruption to him but, after the terrible first month at the home where Graham deteriorated so quickly and now my ECG status being ignored, my trust in the care Graham was receiving had gone.

Packing Graham's clothes and moving him was a big thing to do and I did not take the decision lightly but, Graham falling a fourth time in less than a month, made up my mind for me.

During our notice period, I was blessed with a golden moment. I arrived to take Graham out for the afternoon to find him striding around the home waiting for me to arrive. The striding was amazing in itself as normally Graham shuffled these days but, no, he was striding around. Once we were in the car and on our way to Lowestoft seafront, Graham became very animated and chatty (he could not normally chat) and was very interested in where we were going along with being extremely loving and affectionate.

We drove to Lowestoft seafront, parked in front of the pier and ate our traditional seaside feast of chips, hot doughnuts and soft ice cream in the car.

All the while, Graham was very alert and engaging. This lovely state of affairs lasted about an hour and then he relapsed back into his normal behaviour. As we made the short trip back to the care home for his last night there, he began stuffing the half-pack of left-over chips into the car dashboard and I knew I'd lost him again.

These episodes of clarity and normality became rarer as the dementia took more of his brain and the clear moments were in equal parts wonderful but also unsettling as I started to feel there was more going on in his brain than at first might seem apparent. There wasn't really but it makes you wonder, doesn't it?

It was emotionally painful moving him to the new home; it seemed very final as if this would be the last move for him… little did I know things were about to change dramatically on that front.

Initially, Graham seemed to settle at Pear Tree Lodge and I went in every morning to get him washed and dressed so that there was no friction between him and carers who were not used to his challenging behaviour.

I managed to get him out locally in the car for some fresh air and, on one magical occasion with the help of a wheelchair, I managed to get him inside our new cottage. The expression on his face was a real gift as he sat on the sofa next to me watching old holiday films.

Sadly, within a week of him being at the new home, they had to shut their doors to visitors due to a sickness and diarrhoea bug and that included me. Graham developed it too and I can only imagine what it was like for him in his confused state being isolated in one room. It must have been hell for Graham being shut away from the other residents in a strange new environment.

When visitors were allowed back after ten days of shut down, Graham had declined rapidly and I was shocked when I saw the bent fragile man who was being led towards me.

He was clearly shutting down with each new lockdown in the homes.

I came home very upset and looked at the cottage and thought, can I bring him home? What if Covid shuts the home and he just dies in there with no one to hold his hand? The thoughts whirled around in my head but I kept thinking I could not do this; I couldn't cope in Cornwall, what made me think it was going to be any different here in Suffolk?

I had made the huge decision to move Graham into a care home because I felt I was not able to physically cope with Graham if he had a fall at home, which was highly likely, and his aggression was worsening. However, I had now witnessed the reality of the level of care in a residential home and I knew, if I could just find the right help, I could do a better job of caring for Graham at home.

The big difference though was being back in Suffolk meant that I had a great circle of women friends and their emotional support was the missing link that I did not have in Cornwall. It's not the practical help that they offer because, in general, they can't offer that but it's the warm circle of unconditional love that has made a huge difference to me and that gave me the strength to consider bringing Graham home.

That night, I tossed and turned worrying about the best way forward. Eventually, I drifted off into a fitful sleep and was startled awake in the middle of the night to see the most beautiful yellow light surrounding me. I felt as light as a feather in the bed and I completely relaxed as I knew absolutely and with great clarity that, whatever I decided to do, Graham would be all right.

The next day, I took Graham in the car to Sizewell beach for a planned bacon roll treat. Graham kept his eyes shut and didn't move or communicate with me at all during the short ride to the beach and, as we parked up, he put his hands together in a Reiki position and began moving his lips in a silent prayer.

I felt I knew exactly what he was praying for and drove him back to the care home knowing my decision had been made and by-hook-or-by-crook, small tiny cottage or not, Graham was coming home.

*Operation homecoming.

There followed a military-type campaign to make Lilycot a suitable place to bring Graham home to because I knew there could be no turning back this time.

I gave away the furniture in the sitting room and set up a bedroom in there for Graham. I heaved the tumble dryer down from the garage to the house knowing it was going to be in constant use and ordered a wheelchair and equipment from Red Cross until I could get access to help from the local community services.

There was no way I could make the shower suitable for Graham but I reasoned that, all Graham was having now was a strip wash in the mornings, using a commode for toileting, more often just relying on incontinence pads and he was managing, so that's what he would have to do with me at home. In the old days, that is what we did and we all survived, I thought to myself.

Then I turned my attention to finding a live-in carer at a time when carers were thin on the ground because of Covid.

I have said once or twice already that desperation is the enemy of discernment, and I will say it again now. Be careful, be very, very careful.

I had met a carer in Cornwall who I had kept in touch with via Facebook and she responded to my advert for a live-in carer. I felt lucky when she got in touch with me; lucky, because I already knew of someone wanting to come and support Graham and me at home.

Polly (not her real name) was living in Spain when she got in touch, and she said she would happily come for six months to take up the role of live-in carer. I was thrilled. She flew into Stansted the following week and we had a week together at home getting everything ready before Graham was to join us. I took her advice on everything that was needed equipment-wise, hiring a hospital bed, riser recliner chair and bought anything she asked for to make her room comfortable and I took a deep breath of relief that I now had what I needed to make this work for all of us.

I was very clear when I spoke to Polly about what stage Graham was at with his dementia and we had a clear job description that we had both agreed on and she was insured. In the week before Graham arrived home, Polly and I spent a lot of time together which is when things started to change. I don't care what people believe in or don't believe in, that's not an issue for me, but I was surprised to hear repeatedly that the earth was flat, that the lateral flow tests were to destroy our pineal glands and that the twin towers event had never happened. When these views were shared with my friends who visited, I had to say gently, "please try not to be so vocal about your views to my friends." I thought that was reasonable but, apparently not, and a clearing of the air took place that left me wondering what I had taken on.

Never-the-less I was so thrilled to bring Graham home the following Monday that I pushed all my doubts aside and was determined to make it work with Polly and to keep my thoughts to myself about her personal views on life.

Graham was very, very aggressive and difficult to manage when he arrived home and I could see by Polly's reaction that she was not coping well. It was difficult, very difficult, as the person I had employed with experience to care for Graham was clearly well out of her depth and was not coping at all. As I had not been caring for Graham for the past five months, I just assumed I was seeing Graham's new normal. The first night Graham was at home we needed to change him and his bedding three times in an effort to keep him dry and comfortable.

It was not nice, in fact, at times it was scary, as Graham would happily make a fist with a look of murderous intent on his face and strike out at me or anyone trying to help with pad changes or personal care.

After a night of endless aggression and soaking wet beds, I did wonder briefly, could I carry on? Then, I remembered why I had brought Graham home and I knew for me there was no other way to go.

I rang the GP who said she thought Graham most likely had a water infection and prescribed antibiotics.

NB: You need to be really vigilant about urine infections as, when they arrive on top of dementia, they can make a person spiral out of control mentally and this is what happened with Graham.

Slowly, though, as the antibiotics took effect and with time and patience, things gradually became more manageable.

It was, therefore, a bit of a surprise when, within two days of Graham arriving home, that Polly told me by text that the 'dynamic' in the home did not suit her and she was giving in her notice. Dynamics, my arse; she just could not cope with the hard work that had just landed on her doorstep. I now see in hindsight that, despite my being very clear about how Graham was, she had not really understood his needs and that the reality was not something she was prepared to cope with.

Polly said it was better for Graham and better for me if she went sooner rather than later. I responded that in no way was it better for Graham and I but, clearly, it was better for her so the sooner she left the better.

I was relieved to see her go but stressed beyond measure at having to find a replacement.

My advice;

- Those lines in the sand you made… They all go out of the window when you see your loved one suffering.
- I found that the bowel movements that I felt I definitely could not cope with became an event to be celebrated. I cheered when they happened much like when looking after a young child and it became my new normal with no problem at all. On the positive side, my ability to catch increased too!
- If your loved one's behaviour spirals out of control, it's probably an infection so call the GP as a first line of action.
- There are some great products you can buy to keep the bacteria in the bladder healthy and avoid urine infections. One of them is called Bladapure.
- If your personal circumstances enable you to care for your loved one at home, do it. You have time and you have love, the rest will fall into place.
- Read Contented Dementia as it will teach you all manner of distraction skills that will make your life one hundred percent easier.
- Watch Teepa Snow YouTube videos, they will teach you so much.
- Ask for a continence nurse to assess your loved one and, hopefully, you will be able to access pads in this way.

Chapter 12

WHERE IS THE HELP?

To be honest, I had not really thought I would get any help from the NHS with Graham at home. I knew when I made the decision to raise funds by selling our family home that this would mean I was self-funding. This is something we can explore later in more detail but, for now, I will say that I believe the NHS is wrongly absolving itself of the responsibility to care for dementia patients and is neglecting almost a million patients and their families by not funding care for families like mine. Dementia has a diagnosis, a pathology and devastating physical consequences, so how can this scandalous state of affairs be accepted in a country that prides itself on its health care?

I was reasonably well-informed so I just assumed we would be on our own. I quickly found out that we were ***totally*** on our own, aside from telephone numbers that you could ring that lead to nowhere other than a long chat that results in… nothing.

Two exceptions, I am lucky to have a great GP practice that we were now registered with and a lovely GP that responded to my telephone calls if I made one.

We also have an Occupational Therapist (OT) who came out to assess Graham at home and supply us with all sorts of equipment, so I would no longer have to pay for a bed, hoist and various other items to help us at home.

Because of our need for incontinence protection, we passed the assessment from the continence nurse and they gave us a supply of incontinence pads which saved money and which I was grateful for.

In the first week at home, Graham had a fall. He had been nocturnal for a long time and I quickly found out he was still a night owl. I had been given a baby monitor by a friend and I could hear him moving around via the monitor which I plugged into my bedroom but, by the time I got downstairs, he was on the floor. This was a big problem as he could not follow instructions in any way so I could not get him up.

I had no option other than to call 999 and we waited eight hours on the floor for the crew to get to us.

I made us up a little camp with duvets and cushions and we just had to sit it out with large amounts of sedatives to calm him and we got through. One of those nights, I have wiped from my memory…

Our helpful occupational therapist mentioned that getting a Raizer lift might be an option for us after she realised how long we had been on the floor and I researched them the following day online and gulped at the cost of £1500. Still, I figured if I only used it once and it saved us the nightmare of being on the floor for eight hours again, it would be worth it.

It's brilliant and I heartily recommend them to you. Practice using one before you need it though otherwise, like me, you will struggle to read the instructions at four a.m. especially with your loved one laying on the floor.

During the initial period of Graham being cared for back at home, we received a call from our new GP followed by an in-person visit. I made fun of this personal visit by putting flags outside the door as a mark of the specialness we felt receiving a home visit. She took it all in good fun and we got down to the serious discussion as to why she was visiting us. It was a good day for her to visit, by chance, as Graham was asleep and unresponsive. The GP checked him carefully and decided he was just "very deeply asleep." As luck would have it, Graham's son, Martin, and his family were with us on the day she came so I was able to have this important discussion with Martin present and he completely agreed with the decisions I was making.

Do Not Attempt Cardiopulmonary Resuscitation (DNACPR) are a new term for what I knew as a Do Not Resuscitate (DNR) form.

It was a very big thing to do but I felt relieved when it was in place, as it would not be in Graham's best interests to keep him alive if his body was shutting down. These things must be formally written and kept in a safe place in the house so that, anyone entering medically, would be able to see at a glance what was agreed as the best pathway for Graham.

Luckily, we had discussed this together over the years so I knew it was what he wanted. If you have not had this conversation with someone who can represent your views, please do so, as it will save you a lot of distress in the future.

Having signed the form on Graham's behalf, we were then referred to a local hospice team, district nurses and community teams. None of which we ever saw until the last week of Graham, s life but we were apparently on their radar.

The night Graham was on the floor for eight hours, I was signposted to a team that would be able to help with emergency cover but, when I got through, I was told that they were very sorry, but they currently had no capacity to help me.

See what I mean about the help!

On a lighter note, we began to have golden moments as soon as Graham was at home. Little things, like having to come down in the middle of the night to respond to Graham's banging on the door at two a.m., four a.m. and six a.m. resulted in Graham taking an interest in me in my nightwear with a familiar glint in his eye. I responded by giving him a twirl, and said, "Do you like my night dress?" He replied with a smirk, "You do not need it, darling!" That's my boy!

During the first few weeks Graham was at home, we made a few trips out in the car to Southwold Pier and to Aldeburgh but Graham found these outings stressful so I quickly stopped doing them.

It was also very stressful looking for live-in care as Covid was still with us, making the pool of carers less than it would normally be. The carers that were free to come at short notice were the carers that you really did not want in your home but there was no denying I needed help. No one can care twenty-four-seven without burning out and I knew I needed to keep fit or Graham would end up back in a home.

I had learnt my lesson after the first disastrous experience of acquiring a live-in carer casually and this time decided to use an agency which had a good reputation locally to find a carer with the right level of experience for Graham's needs.

Graham's disease was at the advanced level and I impressed upon the agency that the carer would need to be experienced with challenging dementia symptoms or they would find it hard to cope and provide us with what we needed. I was reassured at the time that they did indeed have carers available who were exactly what I needed. I tried to be positive but the experience of my own 'hands-on' experience of being a community carer had taught me that, excellent training does not, in itself, make for a good carer; what we needed was experience.

Despite this conversation, the first carer I was sent the details of was fresh out of their ten-day carer training with no prior experience of care work, let alone dementia care work.

I declined this first inexperienced carer and was then offered another carer who was to arrive the following Monday.

Olu arrived in our lives two months after Graham arrived home from the residential care home he had been in for five months. Olu was very experienced and, importantly, had experience with challenging behaviour as he had worked with autism and ADHD. This proved useful as all his skills were challenged and utilised during his time with us.

As I opened the door to greet our new carer, I was treated to a wide beaming smile attached to a very large six foot four inch man. I thought, 'oh, my goodness, this is going to be fun.'

Fun, because we have narrow seaman-type stairs, low beams and a small shower and bathroom. Olu, our new carer, carried his large suitcases up the narrow stairs but, to his credit, he said, "Don't worry, madam, it's all going to be fine." In addition, I tightly crossed my fingers behind my back.

Lilycot swayed on its foundations several times in those initial few weeks. The kitchen, small but perfectly formed was used for the first time since I had moved in, not by me, but by Olu, as various stews made with meat from African shops in Ipswich and Norwich were lovingly prepared and cooked in the small kitchen. Who knew such meats existed? Not I, but I do now, and they were accompanied by bucketloads of rice consumed throughout the day to keep the gentle giant happy in his post.

Olu was booked to be with us for three weeks and, during that time, his relationship with Graham became a beautiful thing to behold. What Olu lacked in English-cooking skills (he had none) and various other criteria for the post, he more than made up for with his gentleness, kindness and the high level of dignity that he cheerfully provided to Graham throughout the day. The lack of English cuisine skills forced me back into a cooking role myself for Graham and, by doing so, the cottage began to feel like a home rather than the 'just a place to live' it had been when I arrived. Having had the previous experience of a disastrous carer, helped me to make the best of our new carer and ignore the less-than-great bits. My bar was now set pretty low and that meant to me that, as long as Graham was cared for and given as much time as he needed to avoid aggression, I was happy and, boy, was he cared for well, being treated just as his surname suggested, like a king.

Graham was still aggressive on a daily and sometimes hourly basis. He was very unpredictable and would strike out at Olu and me from time-to-time, but these episodes were very quickly and calmly defused by Olu's calmness, accompanied very often by a gentle message of, "No, Mr King, you love Mrs King and don't want to hurt her." Words are somewhat irrelevant to Graham but the energy from Olu, combined with his kindness to me at those times was gold dust.

The only slight problem waiting in the wings was that Olu was only scheduled to be with us for three weeks but we all seemed to suit each other, so Olu said he could stay until 5th January and I breathed a sigh of relief. When December came, I received an email from the agency telling me the carer replacing Olu was another carer fresh out of training with no prior experience other than, 'used to run his own restaurant.'

Argh!

I discussed it with Olu, and he agreed we needed an experienced carer due to Graham's challenging behaviour and needs and I hinted that maybe he would consider staying but, at that time, he was set on carrying on to his next planned client, so I didn't press him on it.

Olu's background included working with autistic people, working in a nursing home and in clients' homes. This made him the excellent carer he was and he agreed with my view that we needed experience, otherwise the carer would be unhappy and so would I as Graham's needs would not be met.

It quickly became apparent that the agency was not going to offer me anyone else, saying they were happy their training was sufficient when I knew it was not going to be. I voted with my feet and started looking for a carer privately again.

My stress levels began to rise as finding a carer privately when you're getting increasingly desperate is a nightmare and then, one morning, I sensed a change in Olu's energy and I asked him if he would consider staying on.

He responded that he had been thinking about it and that he would give me an answer in forty-eight hours.

Hallelujah!!

Forty-eight hours passed and Olu decided he would stay until mid-summer 2022.

That was fantastic news and I cannot tell you what a weight was taken off my shoulders.

In hindsight, I can see that Olu was sent to us as the perfect person and it was a lesson to me, once again, that spirit will help when asked but the help might not be quite what you might have imagined.

Olu and I worked together in harmony putting Graham's needs at the forefront of our minds at all times. He was a valued, appreciated member of 'team king' and I missed his massive presence when he left us.

Compromise has been a major part of making the relationship between Olu and me work as we have many differences but, overall, we have much more in common than our differences of a spiritual nature might suggest. Olu has adapted to our healer household despite being a Born Again Christian and he feels the Angels are with us, as do I.

Much has been written about healing and the idea that Born Again Christians are opposed to our work as healers. In our home, we had no such problems and found there to be no conflict at all between us. Olu is an open-hearted, open-minded man who knows and understands the unconditional nature of the love we all share in our home.

Graham's journey in early 2022 was now much more about the spirit and less about the physical, as his physical self-diminished. He had seen his late mother appear next to the bed and held out his arms with a smile to unseen friends in the room during the day and night. When these magic times happened, the expression on Graham's face is as that of a child looking at a Christmas tree—pure delight.

When he was awake, he made a beeline to sit in his special chair in the healing room where he drifted straight off to a secret world that I could not, at present, join him in. I have no doubt he is being visited by others in spirit in preparation for his passing and I am at peace with that realisation, as I know that it is an inevitable ending to his illness.

That said, there is a life to be lived and we experience mini miracles almost daily.

Miracles, such as not being able to stand and then suddenly being able to walk across the room carrying his walking frame, rather than using his frame, to help him walk around. Greeting me late at night when I check on him with arms outstretched, saying, "Darling, there you are," are priceless to me, even if he drifts off within minutes. Events such as these are the things that quality of life is built on and I am grateful for all the little miracles that I witnessed daily and also very grateful that I'm privileged to have been able to bring Graham home for the end of his journey. Graham only spent five months in the residential care home but the difference in his life when he was back in his own home was immeasurable.

My own life totally changed, of course, but it was only a phase of my life and this too would pass. It gives me great satisfaction and peace that I did my very best for my soul mate and husband during the last part of our marriage.

I am blessed.

My advice;

- Plan where your carers are going to be sourced from.
- Consider buying a Raizer lift device for the inevitable falls.
- Think ahead and prepare relevant paperwork such as a DNACPR.
- Are you planning for your loved one to pass away at home?
- If so, ensure your community nurse team and GP know this.

Chapter 13

LIFE AT HOME

Our days and nights slipped into an unpredictable but comfortable routine, with Graham leading the way.

Graham was up most of the night walking around his bedroom, which meant that he would spend large parts of normal waking hours sleeping. He kept himself busy at night, rearranging the furniture and generally being active during his nocturnal wanderings and would then sit silently on the side of the bed with hands in a prayer position, exhausted after a full night's work; waiting for me or the carer to arrive to help him.

Life was not without its excitements! One night, the TV suddenly blasted out of the monitor as Graham had turned the TV on but could not turn it off. Another night, I woke up sweating as he had turned up the remote for the central heating to maximum! I soon learnt to take the controls out of his bedroom when he went to bed but he could still fiddle with the control of the bed and that meant a dangerously high bed but, hey, these things could also happen in a care home, and we used crash mats to break his fall.

Music formed a big part of our daily lives and we used an eclectic selection of music during the day.

First thing in the morning, Best of Louis Armstrong was a favourite or, if we were all feeling good, Good Morning Starshine by Oliver.

All personal care took place on his bed, as the shower was too small in the cottage for Graham to use.

Graham was in pads twenty-four-seven and no longer had the agility to use a commode, which was just as well as this was a flashpoint and, the sooner we got the pad changed, the better.

Breakfast was usually served in front of the TV, three Weetabix's and a couple of slices of toast and marmalade. Graham could not follow the news or read newspapers anymore, as he could not understand what they were saying and his ability to read had declined to simple sentences only.

After breakfast, Graham would usually take a snooze that could last until late morning.

When he awoke from his snooze, he would then be out of bed and walking around with his frame or sometimes carrying it like a handbag.

Coffee time—we would have coffee and a treat. I reckoned if you cannot enjoy treats at this stage of dementia, then life would have lost all its pleasure for Graham, and I was not prepared to let that happen.

Midday lunch—I changed the main meal to lunchtime, as Graham loses his appetite as the day goes on and he is often too sleepy to eat late afternoon.

After lunch, singing along with Alexa, we often sang along to songs we had enjoyed at the memory choir. I assumed he still liked singing as he could not tell me one way or another but he would soon yell, “shut up!” if something was not to his taste!

One of the dancing favourites with Olu was ‘Ride’ by Regard… it’s very upbeat and Graham loved watching Olu dance.

After lunch, Graham would usually make it clear by his body language that he wanted to sit in the healing room and I lit a candle, put some oils in the burner and chose something from Bliss or specific healing music. A Hundred Thousand Angels was one of his favourites.

We have always had a healing room in our home since we met and began living together in 2000 and we still have a very small but lovely one at Lilycot. It is full of our collection of much-loved crystals and the energy in there (formed by our work and our intention) is very strong. I have taken some lovely photographs of Graham asleep in his special chair and you can clearly see the energy playing around his head as he sleeps. Alice, our lovely little Jack Russell terrier, is omnipresent and routinely licks Graham’s head as if to try to help him. When she is not doing that, she sits quietly on the arm of his chair like a cat just keeping as close as possible in case Graham should need her. If I have gone into another room and Graham wakes, she hurries out to alert me. She is a magnificent and devoted nurse.

Rocky, our young Jack Russell, dispenses his magic by rushing around the place to cheer us all up.

Mid-afternoon after the healing room snooze, Graham wakes and has a cup of tea with a treat, of course.

Tea/supper is with Bradley Walsh and The Chase followed by Neighbours if Graham is still awake.

Six-thirty p.m. ready for bed—yes, it is early, but it is not my timing. Graham is usually exhausted by then and, just like an infant, there is no hope of keeping him awake when he wants to sleep.

All timings in the day are Graham's and, if I had tried to enforce my timings on him, it would have caused agitation, which would, in turn, have made my life harder.

It is very much like having an infant in the house but sadly,, of course he will not grow out of it and the only ending will be his passing into spirit.

Each day was challenging as things could change very quickly. It is a very skilled balancing act and, if I did not have the skills to manage Graham's condition, then we would have had to have received a large amount of input from the multidiscipline team. As it is, because I do have the skills required, they do not have to come in and I am penalised by not being granted CHC funding that would have had to be provided if I were not here.

Sometimes Graham's appetite was good, sometimes not at all and my decision is always quality of life-based so, if he wants to eat, that is fine and, if not, then that is fine.

We go through large amounts of ice creams and Olu has become adept at getting Graham to look longingly at me when ice cream was mentioned, and they both enjoyed the treat together.

We had challenging but humorous moments when Graham would greet Olu with a half-hearted 'Glasgow kiss'—a head butt to you and me—and then giggle and follow it with an air kiss or he will bunch his hand into a fist and say to him, "how many do you want then!" Luckily, Olu takes it all in good humour and I learnt to be light on my feet to get out of harm's way. The out-of-control days happened in general when Graham first came home and I would suggest you are vigilant about suspected infections such as urine infections or feeling off-colour, as these things make the challenging behaviour become impossible behaviour and can happen very quickly

The incontinence nurse recommended a powder to be mixed into Graham's cereal that balances the bacteria in his bladder and, fingers crossed, it averted all urine infections since that first dreadful one, it is called Bladapure D-Mannose and it has definitely worked well for us.

The district nurse booked Graham in occasionally to have a routine blood test. On one occasion I wasn't at home when she called but Olu regaled me later with the fact that Graham had shouted very loudly at her at the prick of the needle and told her to "F*** off!" Both Olu and I found it very amusing, as Graham is such a gentleman and never swore before dementia.

Did I do the right thing having Graham at home? Absolutely, for us.

By having Graham at home, I had the pleasure of seeing glimpses of the old Graham as he flits in and out of lucidity and those moments made all the hard work all worthwhile.

Did I have doubts about my decision to bring Graham home? Yes, I have occasionally thought if I'd left him in a residential home he would have died earlier and maybe that would have been the kindest thing, but I have always believed it's not that we die, it's the way that we die that's important, so I'm at peace with it now.

I used to ask myself, would we make it through? Of course, but I may well be a very different person at the end of this long journey with dementia.

I was once again forced into the role of a person who is all things to all people in our little bubble of care. This is a role that I gained plenty of practice with when my son was ill with leukaemia for three years, I've also had plenty of time to 'step up' for the past eight years as Graham gradually slipped away from me but, as a bonus, I now have many more skills than I had before our dementia adventure.

Please do not feel you cannot do as we did, because you can; the bottom line is, our loved ones only need love, compassion and time. You may not have the extra skills that I have, but then the community teams would have to come and support you.

There were plenty of hidden blessings, one of which was that I can now carry out most minor DIY jobs and, for those that I cannot manage, I just must pay someone to do the job for me or they are not done. I do not feel resentment at this state of affairs (and that is not because I am a saint) but because I was tortured seeing Graham's decline in the residential home and anything was better than that to my mind. I am full of gratitude that I was of the age where I could learn new things and look after us both.

Graham's quality of life slowly but surely improved once he was back in his own home environment. What had been lost mentally cannot be regained with dementia but, in general, he regained his strength and the ability to walk around most days with his walking frame for the first six months at home, as long as he was accompanied twenty-four-seven due to the risk of falls. We did have bad days when aggression was a constant companion but, by becoming confident with the use of the drugs that had been prescribed by our excellent GP and using them in a bespoke way, I was able to optimise his quality of life.

Be aware that your loved one may be in pain but cannot tell you. Pain can manifest as aggression so do not assume they are not in pain just because they cannot say so. Do not be frightened to use painkillers or pain relieving patches as things progress. Better to be slightly sleepy out of pain than awake and in pain.

There were some evenings when Graham was so frail and tired that I honestly did not think I would find him alive in the morning. I will be honest and tell you that, when I went to sleep at night, I always asked for the highest good to be given to Graham and, if that was for him to be set free from his physical body, then that was okay with me. Although his quality of life was improved by being at home, I cannot honestly say that Graham would think that he had quality of life. In fact, I am sure that he would say he did not. I have never held the belief that death is the worst thing that can happen to you.

I knew that, if I was to survive the inevitable passing of Graham, then I needed something to channel my grief into. Grief, I have found, is just love with nowhere to go and when Sam, my son, died aged ten in 1998, I found my way through it by helping other families with cancer and ultimately working with others like us in the hospital setting. So, knowing this, I have continued to work quietly in the background with the charity Graham and I had created in 2006. I know the charity will be my life raft in the future and, so, I have continued to run training courses and place new projects into the NHS within cancer care. I planned to continue our work when I am alone in the future.

I supported myself spiritually by sitting in regular mediation in our healing room and by attending a local meditation group run by my good friend, Sally. I also receive in-person healing and absent healing from the many friends that support Graham and me on Facebook.

*Absent Healing.

As you know, both Graham and I have worked as healers for many years, both privately and within the NHS. Whilst what we did was hands-on therapy, absent healing is a powerful tool and, whilst I could and did provide hands-on healing for Graham when he would accept it at home, it was obvious to me that the healing and love that was being directed at us both from our many friends on Facebook who are following our journey, was helping to sustain us as we travelled through this part of dementia.

Absent Healing can be seen as friends sending positive thoughts or a prayer, and is offered for someone who is sick; it is perhaps the simplest form of Healing. This form of healing works on the principle that, at least in part, 'energy follows thought.'

We had so many people thinking of us in their prayers and thoughts that the energy we receive is very powerful and it was easy to see the difference it made to Graham's well-being along with my own, especially when I posted a message on Facebook asking for help in this way.

Absent Healing is simple to do for yourself and I offer you the following guidance if you are interested in helping your loved one in this way. Anyone can do it, so please try it.

Practising absent healing—some suggestions;

- Find a warm, comfortable place where you know you will not be disturbed. Turn off the answer phone or unplug the phone, tell others in your household that you will not be available for however long you

state. If you have allocated a special space in your home for healing activities, then use this. It is important to remember, however, that absent healing can be given anywhere, at any time and in any place.
Sending absent healing;

- Visualise the person to whom you want to send healing to, so you can form an energetic link. Inside your head, lovingly invite the person into the healing light that you are sending to them. Alternatively, you might choose to have an image of them standing in a bright beautiful light. It is helpful if you can imagine them in a state of wellness and wholeness.

  After about fifteen minutes or when you have finished, draw the image of healing light back into your heart. Take the light to your feet and feel your feet against the floor. Breathe deeply and bring the session to an end, by rubbing your hands together.

It is tough being alone at home even with live-in care, no one was going to rescue me and no one, it seems, is going to help pay the £1000 a week it costs to keep Graham at home. There are several telephone lines that support carers but absolutely no one in a practical sense, aside from the community team who provide me with equipment and the community nurse who calls once a week either by phone or to call in if we have a physical concern.

There are thousands of people like us just getting on with it at home and we are, in the main, just left to cope. It really is not good enough, is it?

List of helpful tips;

Motor skills decline quickly in the late stages of dementia.

- Twiddle Mittens for hands—stops the hands pulling incontinence pads off.
- Twiddle mat—same, but you can lay it on the table in front of your loved one.
- Comfort life-size baby doll.
- Knife, fork and spoon designed for dementia patients.
- Some people get on with a Tommy Tippee-type cup for drinks. Graham never did but would drink off a spoon in the very late stages.
- NB: I could always find anything I needed on Amazon.

Chapter 14

SPECIAL PEOPLE

There have been wonderful carers that have made a lasting impression on me; Kelly is one of them. I have asked her to contribute to this book and she has written the following account.

KELLY'S STORY

A mutual friend introduced me to Angie and Graham through a recommendation. Angie was looking for someone to look after Graham for a weekend while she taught a course in Hertfordshire.

Little did I know, an adventure was to begin on a road I had not been down before and the most rewarding time I could ever have imagined!

Over the telephone, Angie told me a bit about Graham and what she was looking for and I told Angie a bit about myself; that I was a mum of two boys, one at university, the other going to university the following year.

I explained I did not really have any experience with dementia and no qualification in any form of care, just life experience. I had, however, cared for my closest friend's disabled daughter for about five years, some private care for elderly clients, and my, who had frontal lobe brain damage from a car accident. He, subsequently, became alcohol dependent, which further damaged his brain over the years, making his memory very poor and his behaviour difficult; not unlike Frontal Lobe Dementia.

We arranged for me to visit so I could meet them in person and I felt instantly at ease with Angie and Graham, both very calming, lovely people.

Graham looked fit and well and not what I was expecting at all.

Angie told me about the life they had together and Graham joined in at times with short sentences or nodded in agreement.

If I had not been told differently, I would not have ever thought Graham had moderate dementia at that point.

That aside, he did show small signs without Angie by his side interpreting that he was not communicating as he once could, but I felt confident I could care for Graham and keep him safe for the weekend requested.

Graham had lost his sense of danger so keeping him safe and happy was Angie's main priority.

Graham loved music, listening and singing and so do I, so it was a good place to start to make a connection.

There was a choir set up by the memory café in the local village for anyone affected by dementia, which Graham went to, and a men's-only indoor bowls club, also run by the memory café in the community centre which he loved attending. He was really, good at the bowling and very competitive too!

I joined the choir and went with Graham to join his world and connect with him so we would be able to communicate about the experience when I took care of him in the future.

The choir experience was so uplifting for everyone there; I would recommend trying a choir of any kind for yourself or anyone else, as the benefits were truly amazing.

I discovered Graham could sing whole songs word-for-word and read the lyrics as though dementia had never crossed his path; a different part of the brain apparently for music to speech, I learnt.

Angie lent me a book to read called Contented Dementia and I think it is a useful insight into a world I had not investigated before; it helped me tremendously with my time with Graham.

The weekend came for me to take care of Graham and their two gorgeous doggies while Angie was away.

Angie had left me some photo albums of Graham's life and their joint life photos explaining the family so that, when Graham showed them to me, I could not only ask questions but answer them too. There was a good chance he may not be able respond, through his lack of speech and memory, that way, he would not get distressed if he could not tell me. I found my own way, diplomatically to do this.

That first weekend and, after Graham's breakfast, we took a thirty-minute walk with the dogs and, as we walked, I started to sing a few of the songs we sang at the choir and

Graham joined in. This then became our normal routine, which uplifted us both but also made it less of an issue that Graham could not really talk much so, instead of him trying to make conversation that he could not really convey, we just enjoyed the singing.

As I have got to know Graham, I understood what to talk about and how best to communicate with him; this did change over time, as his capacity changed, I learnt to adapt, but that was later.

After the walk, a cuppa and well-deserved biscuits and more singing with the choir book of forty-nine songs, before we knew it, it was lunchtime.

Graham is a real foodie, loves all food, as far as I know, well tasty food anyway, especially cakes and ice cream which was always another enjoyable thing to do. We ate a lot of cake together. Angie's view was that Graham should do whatever Graham wanted to do and, if that was eat cake, so be it!

We went regularly to a favourite café of Graham's, and we enjoyed lunch and cake together; I did get rounder as my time went by caring for Graham, but it was worth the extra weight for the journey we took with dementia.

Later in the afternoon, we played indoor boules, somewhat similar to bowling but not quite the same.

Graham thrashed me every game, he was brilliant. Angie had been told he did not like to lose and was very competitive and he did not disappoint!

A tea break and biscuits, followed by another thrashing at carpet boules before evening meal and then

Graham was worn out and ready for TV and chill-out time with the dogs.

We spent the four days more or less the same, with different venues for a cuppa or lunch out or lunch at home, but we did go out every day and Graham enjoyed it all. When Angie came back home, she was very pleased with how happy Graham was, and the dogs too who I had spoilt, of course!

In later times, Graham associated me with going out which, sometimes, was not possible, so tactics were needed to get around that situation when it happened; it came naturally to me so it was never a problem, thankfully.

We agreed for me to come once a week to ensure Angie got a small amount of respite, albeit the weekly shop quite often but far easier without trailing Graham out too.

I continued the choir with Graham too; it was such a fantastic feeling being there and watching the effect on everyone else there.

Angie was planning to move back to where they used to live for more support in the future, but fate stopped it and I continued to care for Graham once a week plus choir.

Covid arrived and lockdown followed; this changed Graham's life so much and the dementia really took hold—paranoia, even with medication was hard to manage, with not much support from the services—all just made life for Graham unbearable at times.

His routine for the choir, bowling and the memory café was stripped away and it was too much for him to understand why; he thought Angie was stopping him from attending and that it was all going on without him.

I started to support Angie and Graham three times a week to help fill the void; we would sing, play boules, go for walks, outings, and eating out was not possible, as everything was closed. Takeaways were open though so we began a new routine of getting a coffee and cake from a takeaway, sitting in the car not far from the house.

We sang to the songs on the radio or CDs, even though Graham's abilities were diminishing, he still tried to sing and did it really well. We engaged with local radio, sent in pictures of us with our coffee cups in a feature called virtual coffee break set up by the local radio in lockdown. We got our names mentioned on air and even did a singing video which the radio played.

We danced, made up actions to songs, different every time, and we laughed a lot.

We were generally just joyful like children, which was where Graham was at mentally by then in his head—the movies we watched were children's movies.

Jess, who was one of the memory support team, started up video chats online of songs we knew and did simple actions to do with the songs, which we watched often.

The choir leader rang every week and tried to sing over the phone, but it was only successful for a short time; it just got too confusing.

The choir did not return during this time because of Covid, ditto the bowling. Eventually, recordings of the songs from the choir were put online and we tried to engage with these. Sadly, it had taken so long to set up this new way of working that, during the interim, the relentless damage from dementia meant that Graham's brain was no longer able to join in online. He needed in-person help and, aside from Angie and me, this was not possible because of Covid.

Once we were able to get out again, we made the most of it and went to see many places we had missed in lockdown. We did this until Graham became too unsteady on his feet to walk anywhere and the use of the toilet requirements became too distressing for him; even a thirty-minute trip out was not possible.

Graham loved clothes and was stylish from top to toe, which became impractical when he required pull-up pants but he was always complimented on his appearance and he loved it. He had a swagger and a look so you knew he was thinking, "Yes, I've still got it!"

During this time, Graham's care needs increased dramatically and he required help daily for personal care. Angie thought my skills with Graham helping to keep his spirit upbeat were best used by continuing that way, so she found Beki, who did a fantastic job helping Graham with personal care.

We became Graham's Angels until Graham really needed full-time care. Angie knew deep down she needed to have a break from caring for Graham, but it was the hardest decision for her.

Angie moved back to her previous hometown where she had support from friends and regained her strength while Graham resided in a care home.

Sadly, the home that Graham was admitted to could not give Graham the attention, stimulation and care we all gave him and his health diminished rapidly. None of us could bear to see the rapid breaking down of his personality and his physicality. Angie took him out of the care home after four months into another care home near her own home where she could visit daily but, Graham continued to fade rapidly in front of her,, so she made the huge decision to move him back in with her and the dogs Alice and Rocky.

If I have any advice for you, it is to understand that 'you' are the best caregiver for your family. Of course, it's not always possible to care for your own family and, sometimes, a care home is the only option. Thankfully, for Graham he has Angie; she has brought him calm, peace and love at home with the help of a live-in carer.

I absolutely loved my time with Angie and Graham. I may have helped them, but they enriched my life with the experience of caring for Graham; it was the most rewarding experience, it never felt like work. I learnt so much, gained friends with two people I would never have had the pleasure to meet otherwise.

Angie's advice;

Do not be frightened to use a carer with no qualifications.

Kelly was adaptable, loving, and patient and cared about Graham… that is the most important thing to look for in a carer.

Chapter 15

CARERS

Aside from gems like Kelly and Olu, carers are a very mixed bunch of people, especially live-in carers. I had thought in my naivety that, as I had money and would be self-funding, that getting a professional live-in carer would be a relatively straightforward matter.

Not so.

The carers that prefer to live-in on the job are often living quite unusual lives themselves and are a very unusual group of people.

One prospective carer had a stable of Arab ponies in Egypt, which meant she needed to work two weeks on, two weeks off, in order to fly back and forth; many other carers I spoke to had similar extravagant lifestyles.

Please do not misunderstand me; I do not begrudge them their salaries but they are an interesting bunch of people, leading quite extraordinary lives.

The rates of pay for carers is a contentious issue and there are some very strong feelings on both sides as to what is a fair rate of pay.

In my case, the salary of £1k per week was at the high end of the scale for many carers but, if you break it down to seven-days-a-week, ten-hours-a-day, it does not equate to more than £15 per hour. All everyday living expenses with a food allowance are extra so, as long as you are happy living in someone else's home, it is a good way to make a living, have a roof over your head and earn a reasonable salary.

When you consider in our own case that the carer has a short day as Graham is asleep much of the morning, several hours in the afternoon and is ready for bed by six p.m., you could reasonably argue that, aside from personal care in the morning, it is not the most challenging or physically demanding of roles.

Over the time that carers have shared my life, my biggest learning curve has been that I had to learn to keep my mouth shut and my thoughts firmly zipped up.

It has taken a great deal of self-restraint from someone like me who has always freely spoken my mind to hear extreme, political views from several of the carers that have worked with us. It has stretched me mentally and emotionally in order to make the arrangement work but has, ultimately, probably contributed to my personal growth!

Having live-in care is expensive so beware the hidden costs of having a carer in the house and lay down your ground rules of what is acceptable early in your relationship. It is your house after all but, like me, you may find that, once they have settled in, you will do almost anything not to offend them for fear they would leave you high-and-dry.

What I have developed during the year of live-in carers is patience and the ability to enjoy the best of them for Graham's sake and leave the rest.

Our first live-in carer (from an agency) liked to be clean.

This meant we went through six bottles of shower gels a week, six bottles of washing-up liquid, copious amounts of detergent and washing powder and, what seemed like, dozens of loo rolls.

Along with personal care, the role required the carer to cook for Graham and to keep his room clean and tidy. Space in our little cottage kitchen is tight but, somehow, we managed to store large amounts of meat and pulses for the carer in order for him to make his personal food.

The carers we used were amongst the messiest cooks I have ever seen and the food with its highly-pigmented herbs and spices was spread over the kitchen surfaces liberally. The carers also liked to fry yams and bananas so Mazola Oil was spread around too. I can inform you that the two things together set like concrete on a hot stove.

With a family member, you could attempt a spot of retraining but not so with carers, as they take offence easily and need gentle ego-flattering handling at all times. If I forgot to do that then the atmosphere dived like a submarine! A bit like a husband, partner or teenager, but with no perks to ease the road!

Breakages were frequent; liquidiser, toaster, a scare with the washing machine and numerous other items all came to a sticky end and had to be replaced.

This particular carer liked to wash their bedding and clothes regularly, which was admirable, and the opposite would have been a nightmare, but Graham's washing was minimal compared to their three washing machine loads a day. This, of course, led to the tumble dryer being in almost constant use and my electricity bill tripled. Everybody does things differently and that is fine but I did get a little tired of hearing the words, "But, Mrs King, I have been trained to work professionally." Just a shame they did not teach them how to make a ham sandwich!

Our special carer, Olu, had said he was able to stay with us until September 2022 as he was saving for his family back home but the leaving date was unexpectedly brought forward one day, when he said, "Mrs King, I need to leave, I am a broken man." I looked at him in astonishment thinking if he was broken I was on the scrap heap but I listened patiently to him telling me why he felt broken and his reason translated quickly into, I need to return to Africa as my fiancé won't wait for me any longer. Whatever the real reason, he left, and I was fortunate that a carer who had filled in when Olu had taken a week off stepped into the role.

Our next carer fulfilled her job description and more and, I must admit, it was heaven for a while. She cleaned, she cooked and she was good with Graham; fantastic. Sadly, her husband had a stroke within three weeks of her being with us and she left without any notice at all.

So, there I was, completely alone, with no help at all, with a husband who some days could stand for personal care and sometimes could not.

When the district nurses came that week, they could see I was struggling and, when I used the magic words, "We are at risk of a fall," they swiftly arranged some help via a team called 'React' based in Ipswich.

React are a team that exists to stop hospital admissions so, as Graham was at risk of a fall, they provided a carer to help with personal care in the mornings for an hour to help avoid a fall.

React was a short-term fix so, once again, I began exploring care agencies.

The one thing that the agencies have in common (or at least the ones I have had dealings with) is that the sales team sell you the dream of an experienced dementia-trained carer available straightaway, but then they do not actually deliver the service. It is a very disappointing experience, especially when you really need help.

The first carer offered to me via an agency was a twenty-year-old young man with no dementia experience aside from having a granddad with dementia. Unsurprisingly, I said, no, thank you, for his sake and for ours. Then, I was offered a lovely woman suddenly available, who was to turn up the following Wednesday at midday. Great, I thought, I could get through one more week on my own and I breathed a sigh of relief. Wednesday came and I could feel the weight of responsibility slipping from my shoulders with the imminent arrival of a carer, only to receive a call from the agency an hour before the expected arrival from their office, saying, that the carer was unable to come as she had woken up very tired and would come the following day.

I think the top of my head blew off at that point!

During that week, whilst I frantically looked for a carer, I received a condolence card from the care company along with a beautiful orchid, two pieces of scrummy cake and a bunch of tulips apologising for the condolence card.

Words failed me; I did not want or need any of that, I just needed a reliable carer.

There then followed a little comedy farce when they tried to persuade me, she was exactly the right person for me, just tired, and to give her a go tomorrow. I said, no, as I felt if she could let me down with no notice, I had no confidence in her commitment as a carer.

Nevertheless, I still needed someone to help me with Graham and so I went back to the Facebook groups where you can find carers and, within a short time, I found Marianne.

Marianne had been a domiciliary carer for some twelve years and, from our conversations, she was clearly on the same page as me when it came to care (or so she said). She could not come for another week but I agreed to wait and looked forward to her arrival.

Once again, we were strangers to each other and, once again, more adjustments were needed for us to get along and to fulfil Graham's needs.

I think I'm fortunate to have had the experience of having worked as a carer when my children were young as this has helped me know what good care is and I am not easily bamboozled by carers saying, I'm doing it this way as my way is best; although they still try and Marianne certainly tried!

After twelve years of domiciliary care, I got the distinct impression that Marianne thought live-in care was going to be easier for her. Of course, it is in some ways, as there is no travelling between clients but, being part of a family, requires different skills and Marianne was very used to getting her own way with no one other than the client to consider. We had conversations about some of her friends that also worked within the homes of clients, and she expressed the view that wives or husbands could be a challenge. Hmm!

I knew Graham very, very, well. I know what would make him respond in aggression and what would give us all a peaceful life. I have found it very challenging to hear strangers, albeit well-meaning, say, 'have you tried stimulating him with this or that?' I bit my tongue and gently explained that we are now in a very different stage of the disease and all Graham needs is love, time, support, and, yes, his wife in this instance really does know best, so listen up!

Marianne was certainly a very loving woman with a big heart, but that heart also stretched to managing other Hungarian friends' lives on the phone for hours at a time during the time she was meant to be looking after Graham.

It was, at times, like a black comedy farce having to manage her forceful personality. On one occasion, we were either side of Graham and she was insisting the cream she had brought from elsewhere was the best cream to protect his skin from breaking down. With Graham playing piggy in the middle and his nightwear displaced, she argued at length with me that her cream was better than the cream that I had in my hand prescribed by the district nurses. In the end, she slapped hers on Graham's skin and short of scraping it off, she had inflicted her opinion once more on me and, of course, Graham.

I have had my share of difficult conversations with carers and most of them centre on the almost constant use of their mobile phones. I do not have a problem with emergency calls but being constantly on the phone when Graham was awake was not okay. There was so much time available to use her phone when Graham was asleep that the constant internet searching and chats online became, to my mind, unacceptable. I finally managed to pluck up courage to address this, only to have her burst into tears and wail at me, "See, you do not love me!" This time, I just laughed aloud and said, "Do not be ridiculous. I absolutely do not love you or, in this instance, your behaviour. I just want you to treat Graham like a human being and interact with him when he is awake. I honestly do not think that is too much to ask."

Even Graham piped up one day and said, as she was shouting her views at me, "I'm still here, you know." Exactly right.

Apparently, it was too much to ask Marianne to do her job and so she told me she needed to leave. "Fine, off you go," I responded, having come to the end of my patience at last. This led to more wailing and I threw a thought up to spirit. "What the heck is going on here? Please stop testing me and send me a carer that is emotionally fit for work and can do the job… it's not rocket science." Marianne then had a quick change of heart and wanted to work out her notice and, because I was desperate, I allowed her to. In the end, after a few months of her high-octane life, I got tired of all the drama, tired of her shouting in my face, saying it was just her Hungarian way and just plain tired of her in the end, and I asked her to leave immediately as she had become unmanageable.

Is it wrong to feel relieved when a carer leaves? I do not know but I did feel relieved, and the house was once again calm. Bliss!

My advice;

- Be mindful that you are inviting a complete stranger to live side-by-side with you and your family in a very intimate setting that involves the personal care of your loved one, not because you want to but because you have to.
- Check references.
- Talk to past employers, if you can, and do not wear rose-tinted desperate glasses.
- Sometimes pop-in carers are better in every way than live-in carers. They at least have normal lives. They proved to be more reliable although

not ideal as our needs were so intense. They only came a few hours during the day which meant the pressure on me definitely increased during this time.

Chapter 16

DIFFICULT DECISIONS

When I was alone with Graham, which I frequently was in the last three months of his life, I had to resort to the difficult decision to barricade him into his bed at night. I could not risk a fall and I could not be up all night and then be on alert all day.

I could manage the days reasonably well if I could just sleep at night. The 'system' strongly disapproves of bars on beds, saying people can get badly hurt. Well, falling out of bed can also result in a nasty situation so I had to make my own system of encouraging Graham to stay in bed at night when I was alone. I found that, once the obvious route out of bed was taken away from him, with two home-made barriers and a couple of high-back chairs placed against the bed, Graham immediately became calmer at night. I do not think he slept any better, but he was content to stay on the bed without the constant compulsion to get out of bed.

With the baby monitor in place to enable me to hear if Graham was distressed, we both slept better at night. I wish I had done this sooner.

When you live with your loved one, you do not really notice that things are going downhill, you just deal with each day as it comes. In hindsight, I can see that Graham was withdrawing from life by sleeping longer and longer during the day, but he still enjoyed his food, as long as he was fed, of course. I do wonder how many of our loved ones starve to death in care homes and hospitals, not because they do not want to eat, but because staff feel they are refusing food when, really, all they need, is time and a willing person to feed them.

How terrible it is then to get so tired through lack of support that you begin to look at your sleeping husband and ask yourself silently… how long will you be with me, darling, as my money and energy are running out?

What a terrible thing to have to consider when death is just around the corner.

This, I believe, is at the heart of the true betrayal of our dementia patients. It is a disgrace that the cost of care hastens our loved one's passing.

Eventually, our savings dropped below the financial threshold and our local council arranged for a social worker to conduct a needs assessment. At that point, July 2022, we had spent nearly £100k on care as self-funders because we did not receive any support from the NHS when we really should have done. I do not begrudge one penny of that money; that is why I sold our home in Cornwall after all, but the system is wrong. It is a shambles and, in many cases, a postcode lottery.

I did not have the energy or the time to fight the decision not to fund Graham's care at the time the CHC assessment had taken place in November 2021; I was too busy trying to get carers and looking after Graham, but I will certainly challenge them when I get the energy to do so.

The social worker who came to carry out the needs assessment in July 2022 was a lovely woman working to implement a policy based on finances and not on what is best for the patient and their families, in my opinion. It is not the social workers' fault, it is the system's fault and it needs changing. We were both frank and open together and she gave us the minimum of what we needed, a middle pathway of help, that would enable me to keep Graham at home with some assistance with the ongoing costs.

This assessment would not happen in cancer care at end-of-life so why are we allowing it to happen in dementia care? Dementia has a pathology, a diagnosis and devastating physical, mental and emotional needs. It is brain death and should be seen as any other brain disease.

It's complete nonsense to say that the patient's needs in the last stages of dementia are simply for social care. Dementia or brain death takes all our loved one's physical faculties eventually so, therefore, it is a physical as well as a social care need that our loved ones have.

That said, I have heard horror stories of Continuing Healthcare Funds being taken away from cancer patients too. If, as someone said, you can judge a society by how it treats its most vulnerable members of society, then humanity has, for the most part, been lost in dementia care.

It was around this time that I started to write a few words that I intended to post on Facebook when Graham passed away.

Facebook has been a fantastic support to me. So much love has been sent our way, as I have shared highs and lows of Graham's dementia journey with my friends on social media. Honestly, I do not think I would have coped so well without every single one of those messages supporting us both and willing us on.

Even though Graham was still eating well, my gut was telling me he would not be here with me much longer. I noticed that his ability to swallow was becoming impaired and I knew this was the end. I did not focus on the pain of that understanding, I just carried on as normal, as I have found that if your energy becomes distressed then so does your loved ones. There would be plenty of time later to feel everything I needed to feel but, for now, we had a life to live.

Something quite wonderful happened during this time and I do not quite know how it happened. Graham's speaking improved. It was very funny when I had to grab hold of him to prevent a fall and he yelled out, "Get off my bollocks!" So, unlike my gentleman husband but so funny.

I had been reminded when Graham first could not recognise me, that his soul still knew me. My close friend, Leonora, gave me this pearl of wisdom and, although I was sceptical at first, I realised in those last few months that it was true; his soul did know me and we were as close, if not closer, than we had ever been. Each time I walked in the room, Graham's face lit up with joy and I felt the same joy in my heart. It was different, very different to how I had felt during the long journey to reach this point but it was beautiful to experience and to see the difference in Graham's energy when I responded to his body language. I would sit or kneel in front of him and place my hand on his heart and say, "I know." His face changed to one of great love and we embraced each other. Graham's experience of touch had changed and his fingers could not function properly but he would reach out to me, cup my head in his hands and, with the utmost gentleness, say very clearly, "I love you, darling, you are so special."

I have never experienced unconditional love before but I have now and it is beautiful. Even when Graham seemed lost, he would surprise me by coming back to me. When I was singing along to the Everley Brothers, I suddenly found Graham joining in with the words, 'dream, dream, and dream' and then he gave me the most beautiful smile. I am lucky to have captured this on my phone so, when two months later he suddenly got very ill, I have that golden moment to look back on.

There were also signs from spirit of his potential passing in the house at this time. A dragonfly flew into the room where Graham slept one day, looked around and then calmly flew out of the door again. Birds came very close to the house and butterflies landed on me in the garden. These were all signs to me and I began mentally preparing as best as I could for the transition that I knew was coming, sooner than I would like.

Apparently, it is a very Aquarian thing to do, to prepare for the funeral when the loved one is still here. I am aware that it is a coping mechanism for me but it is also a desire to do Graham proud and not wait until I was perhaps incoherent with grief and not able to do the right things for him.

This also led me to prepare for his cremation. I researched and investigated pure cremation-type funerals but had not made up my mind about which way to go.

Graham and I discussed it years ago and decided that having an event for people to come to when we have not seen family and friends for most of the years that Graham had been in serious decline, would simply be a waste of our time and money. Therefore, for Graham, I have decided that a simple service with a handful of people who loved and supported us both will be invited to be at the cremation. Following the simple procedure, we will then go and walk somewhere in nature to celebrate and remember the man, not the shell that had just been cremated.

I will do this with the full knowledge that Graham is home and free in spirit.

I know many people will not feel this way, but I am also sure that it was my decision, and I would not be doing something to please others at one of the most difficult times of my life.

I do not think I have mentioned yet that I took the decision to convert our garage to a one-on-one care facility in early 2022. I really thought Graham might be with me for several years yet and wanted him to be in a comfortable room where I could use hoists and give him a shower, so I applied for planning permission to convert an outbuilding to a one-on-one care facility. The builders had been busy doing this for the past six months. We had several delays as the builders had Covid and other health issues that delayed the build, but it was nearing completion.

I had been chatting to Graham for months telling him why the builders were here, what I was doing and saying that he would be able to have a shower after a year of flannel washes and he seemed to like the idea. He certainly liked seeing the builders, as they were friends by now as we had used them for building work when we lived in Suffolk before moving to Cornwall. Graham's face lit up when he saw Stephen and Trevor. I know he probably did not really understand what they were doing but I took him up to visit the building a few times in his wheelchair and he seemed pleased. It gave me something to aim for and I just hoped it would be done before he passed into spirit. At the beginning of 2022, I felt he might live with dementia for some years but then, in August, I could see that was not the case, so the builders made every effort to get the conversion finished for Graham.

THE NEST

Our occupational therapist, Jo, had very kindly arranged for a second hospital bed to be delivered so that we could give Graham the opportunity to settle in the Nest or, if he did not like it, to come back to his usual bed in the house. On the first real visit to the Nest, our neighbours came to have a cup of tea with us. Graham looked happy that day; it was a golden moment. He dozed off to sleep when they left and he seemed happy to stay there. I slept on the floor next to him that night and our first night and day in the Nest seemed to have gone very well. The next day, our pop-in carer, Laura, came and they had a lovely time singing and smiling together whilst I walked the dogs. I felt happy that we had got Graham into the Nest and planned for a shower the next day.

Then the chest infection hit.

My advice;

- Live every day.
- Consider thickening power for liquids.
- Be awake to the signs and final gifts that your loved one is offering you.
- Bespoke meds are the secret to quality of life. Ensure your loved one is not in pain; your GP will help you with this.

Chapter 17

FINAL GIFTS

In the end, death crept up on us quickly.

Graham woke up struggling to breathe two days after we moved into the Nest and sounded very congested in his lungs. I called the GP, and she came to see him after morning surgery that day. Dr Mags and I looked at each other as I greeted her on the drive and we both knew at that moment that the time had come.

I had been using the gun-type thermometer to check Graham's temperature. It was giving a false reading of 37.3° but the GP found he had a temperature of 39.9°.

I threw my thermometer in the bin in disgust and, if you have one, I advise you to do the same.

The GP turned to me and said, "I am sorry but he is very ill." We had a discussion outside to ascertain if Graham should go to hospital and I said, no, as to do so would have put Graham into the situation I had worked so hard to keep him out of for the past year. The GP supported that decision and said, "let's try some antibiotics." Graham managed a few initial doses of antibiotic the first day, along with a couple of treats and ice-cream but then, the following day, he could no longer swallow and refused all food and medication from that point.

I had no live-in carer so the district nurses called in the React team again and they took over Graham's personal care. All that last week of Graham's life, I was trying to arrange another live-in carer for the following week. The stress was enormous and, if we had had CHC funding, as we should have done for what was now, end-of-life care, I would at least have had that stress taken away from me.

We endured seven days and nights of pure torture. Hearing Graham struggle to breathe that last week was terrible. I had imagined that Graham dying at home would be like my son, Sam's death twenty-four years ago, peaceful. This was not peaceful, it was a struggle and, after three days, the decision to put up a syringe driver to help Graham was made but, sadly, it made no difference to the struggle.

Every night, I heard Graham struggle to breathe, and his struggle continued throughout the day. By now, a deadly calm had descended on me, as I knew where we were going, what was happening, and what I needed to do.

I began using aromatherapy oils for transition of his spirit and played appropriate music to calm everything down. I knew he would find these things comforting.

I spoke to him of all the wonderful things he had achieved throughout his life and spoke of the amazing marriage we had enjoyed and how lucky we had been to find each other. I spoke of how joyful those who loved him on the other side would be to be reunited with him and spoke of all those people he had helped with Reiki being there to welcome him when he was ready to let go. I told him I would be all right and would carry on our work and that there would be no separation for us, as we would live in each other's hearts until we were reunited again.

This I believed and I know he did too.

All of this I could see was helping him but witnessing the struggle and determination of his body not to leave that last week was very, very hard. The dogs jumped up on the bed next to him and Alice gave him her most rigorous licking to try to help, whilst Rocky, usually so boisterous, lay quietly beside him.

I alerted Graham's children that their planned visit in two weeks' time should be brought forward and, despite being frank, I do not think they really understood why. Even when they arrived to visit the Friday before Graham passed on the Sunday, I still do not think they realised their father was dying. I have given up trying to understand family members so, when they left after an hour, I just let them go.

Sally, our very good friend, dropped in to see us unexpectedly during that week. Graham had taught Sally Reiki many years ago and we were all very closely linked spiritually. She gave Graham some healing and left, saying I was to call her if I needed her at any time.

The hospice nurses were by now helping the district nurses by dropping in once a day to change the syringe driver and, by mid-week, I asked them if a hospice bed was available and, if it was, would that be better for Graham. They told me that they would only be doing at the hospice what I was already doing at home so I made the decision to carry on, as that is what we had planned when our journey with dementia had begun eight years ago.

I was alone most of that week, aside from the district nurse and React team visits, but I had an inner knowing that this was how it was meant to be, so I just accepted it and carried on. It has always been just the two of us in our relationship and it felt right to be just the two of us at the end of his life.

I experienced a dark night of the soul during that week as I lay listening to Graham's struggle and I thought of those who had ended their loved one's life, as they could not bear to see them suffer. I now understood how they had felt as it passed through my mind to do so. The thought left as quickly as it had arrived, and I knew that was something I could not do. My role was to witness, wait, and support Graham the best way I could and that was simply by being there next to him.

With no live-in carer in place, it was difficult to move Graham and to make him comfortable, so the decision to use a catheter to avoid any unnecessary discomfort was made. I am very grateful for the kindness of the district nurses and React teams who did their best to support us during that last week.

I had been given a spiritual message some months earlier that Sam, my son, would come to collect Graham when the time was right. During those last few days, I was jolted awake at two a.m. one night as I could hear Sam's voice shouting, "Mum, Mum," outside the window. I looked over at Graham but he was just struggling to breathe as normal and he did not pass away until the following day. Did Sam come? Well, I definitely heard him; I could not make up his child's voice but he was outside not inside. I am comforted that he was there at all during that last week.

Sunday 28th August 2022

The struggle continued and I had no way of knowing if I needed a carer to live-in or not for the following week as I did not know how long Graham was going to stay with me. I had to call the nursing teams out for top-up drugs several times a day in those last few days, as Graham was becoming distressed, and I knew he needed more medication to support him. However, that last day, I could not contact the district nurses or the hospice nurses on their systems and a feeling of resignation and acceptance descended on me. I, eventually, got a call back saying they would be there that evening but they could not tell me when.

During that final morning, I finally found a carer called Eunice who was due to arrive at the local train station at eight p.m. that night. She had travelled from Devon to be with us and Mark, my neighbour, went to the train station to pick her up.

Eunice was, without doubt, an angel and, during the evening, we sat in vigil together sharing stories about Graham and our lives. About ten p.m., Eunice left to go to the house and rest and I set about making a cup of tea to sit next to Graham.

As I sat down next to the bed at ten-forty-five p.m., I was immediately aware that Graham's body was alert, his eyes had opened, and his breathing had changed. I dropped the tea and grabbed his hand and said to him, "Here we go, Graham, it's fine, just let go, all is well." I spoke to him calmly as he made his transition and he was free at last.

I sat with Graham for a while, watching the signs of death pass over his body and then called Eunice and she came straight back up to the Nest.

She was clearly very shocked that Graham had gone so quickly but her presence there with me was a gift and I will always remember her for her grace during the week she stayed with me following Graham's passing.

The hospice nurse arrived at eleven-forty-five p.m. to find we no longer needed her. She checked Graham and confirmed his death.

I asked Eunice to go and bring the dogs up and they calmly said their goodbyes and jumped off the bed after another good licking by Alice.

I rang Sally and asked her whether she would come to help me wash Graham. Without a moment's hesitation, she said, "I'm on my way."

Sally arrived to help me lay Graham out and freshen him up. This was something I wanted to do, and I could ask no friend for more than Sally gifted us both at that time.

As we preformed the time-honoured role of laying out a loved one, I was calm and almost happy that Graham was at peace and would suffer no more. We dressed Graham in what I knew he would like, until finally there was no more to be done other than to wait for the funeral home to come and take Graham into their care.

After they had left, I slept well for a few hours, safe in the knowledge that Graham was home and free at last.

Chapter 18

AFTERWARDS

The night after Graham died; I was woken up in the middle of the night by a very loud banging on the bedroom wall next to my head. It was incredibly loud but, surprisingly, I did not feel any alarm. I felt at peace and went straight back to sleep. I knew it was my magic man calling just letting me know all was well.

Eunice, the carer who I no longer needed, stayed with me that first week. I did not have the heart to turn her away, but I believe she was sent by spirit to be with me. She was the Angel by my side in those first few days without Graham and, when the time came for her to leave, I was very sad to see her go. She cleaned, she made endless cups of tea and she was just there… just what I needed.

When the Queen died on the 8th September, it felt entirely right to me that most of the world was now in mourning too.

Whilst I waited for the world to start turning again, I made a visit to Walsingham in Norfolk. Graham and I had visited there several times during our lives together and we had always felt drawn to visit when times were tough. I felt compelled to visit the shrine and to light candles for

Graham before his cremation the following week. It was nice, not particularly meaningful, but nice and the dogs had a run on Holkham Beach so it was a lovely day out. I am smiling as I type, nice, as Graham used to use the word, 'nice,' to express a feeling at times and I used to tease him and say, nice! Nice is a biscuit, not an emotion!

It is a strange feeling when a loved one has passed after a long illness. People try to be helpful and offer their thoughts on the matter in the vein of, 'You must feel relieved that his suffering is over?' Or 'You are free now to get on with your life.' One particular friend said to me, "but he wasn't your dear Graham at the end, he was your baby."

Well, no. I did not feel any of these things. I was in the void. The void is a place I'm familiar with; where time is meaningless and you just keep breathing and eating a little with no real sense of anything except mind-numbing loss. I spent a year in the void following my son, Sam's death in 1998 so I recognised the feeling of being wrapped in bubble wrap and just existing until I was strong enough to step forward again.

In fact, reflecting back on that huge loss (Sam was ten when he passed) helped me to cope with the loss of Graham. In all honesty, the loss was manageable because Graham had experienced a reasonably good span of life whereas Sam had not. Comparisons are not relevant other than I knew that, if I could survive losing one of my children, then I could certainly survive this. I was also comforted that I had less time to live without Graham than

I had had to endure by losing Sam as a child, as it would not be long before I would make my own transition and join them both in spirit.

Graham, at the time of his death, was still very much the man I loved and will always love, despite his illness turning him into a dependent infant to all intents and purposes. I loved him more as a soul mate and husband at his passing than perhaps I had done throughout the twenty-two years we had shared each other's lives.

Grief is such a personal thing and words are, at best, meaningless. Just standing beside someone in his or her grief is the best gift we can offer each other. That and not being afraid to talk about the person who has passed is probably the best gift you can give the bereaved.

The week after my visit to Walsingham, I went to see Graham in the chapel of rest before his cremation later that week.

It was a challenge and the tears flowed. Despite my leaving instruction to the funeral directors not to touch him, they had felt that they needed to do something with his mouth, and he had the most un-Graham type smile on his face. Nevertheless, I did what I had gone for and that was to ensure it was Graham in the coffin and to put some keepsakes in his hand for the journey ahead. I covered his body with a beautiful scarf and kissed him goodbye for the last time on earth. Of course, he was not there but it comforted me to do so.

Graham's cremation was beautiful. Full of meaningful music and a poem written by his late father as a love poem to his son, along with a beautiful poem by Donna Ashworth.

There were eight of us there, including my dear friend, Leonora, who took the service in her role as a multi-faith minister.

It felt completely right, and I was glad that I had not given in to pressure to do something not aligned with my beliefs.

It was and is the strangest of feelings to have lost my great love and not to be completely overwhelmed with grief.

Maybe this is because I've been grieving for four or five years since the dementia really took hold but I believe it's more likely that I do not feel huge loss because he has not really gone. Yes, of course, his physical body has gone but his love, energy and essence surround me in a warm bubble of protection.

Therefore, that leaves me no choice other than to 'walk the talk.'

I have started to pick up the threads of my life and opened the spiritual group in my local town as planned and I am running workshops for our charity as our charity work continues.

My dogs are wonderful companions and sense when I am sad, cheer me up and insist on going out for walks, which is all good therapy for me.

I am lucky. I have a cottage to live in and just about enough money to pay my bills. I have friends to make me laugh when I need lifting up a bit and I do not feel alone, ever, I have spirit within me and beside me. I believe that, for those who truly love, there is no separation, only love.

In addition, so be it.

POSTSCRIPT

Would I choose to care for Graham at home again if I had to? Yes. The emotional rewards far exceeded all the difficulties.

Would I advise other families to do the same? Yes.

However, I am now challenging the CHC authorities regarding their refusal to fund Graham's care as, for every person like me who can stand up and say that is wrong, there are hundreds and thousands of other families struggling to cope with a loved one with dementia.

If Graham had suffered from a brain tumour, which was destroying his brain, his care would have been funded. Because it was dementia, it was not. This is wrong on so many levels and I will do all I can to challenge and change the way dementia is viewed by the NHS.

DON'T MISS ME MORE

By Donna Ashworth

Don't miss me more than once a day,
For life is moving fast.
Don't wish all of your time away,
Dreaming of the past.

Don't waste the moment looking at
The things I left behind me.
I'm not within those walls or boxes
The heart is where you'll find me.

Don't dread to say my name, sweet one,
Don't fear the wrath of sadness.
Just take the love you had for me,
And turn it into gladness.

Don't worry when my birthday comes,
Don't feel me missing more.
I'm filled with love you're sending me,
Just as I was before.
Some days your anger will rush out,
Your tears will find their way.
To me, wherever I am then.

I'll soothe them all away.

When I am gone, don't miss me more
Than once, or twice a day.
There's so much life to live, my love.
I'm with you, all the way.

And finally Graham touched many people's lives with his gift of Reiki, he was truly a magic man.
Our special friend Declan has written this beautiful poem to honour Graham.

The magic man, taking his part in the holy healers plan
A thoroughbred, thundering down the track
Onwards in peace
His soul released
To fly with the angel of the eternal sky
Questions 'why' drop away
Listening to compassion today.

Gentle giant of a man
He answered the call for the healing plan
No sickness or death, we have eternal breath
Bound by celestial chords of healing light
We carry on now with spiritual sight.

Trust the process, deep we go
an onwards journey in a mystical show

Actors on the universal stage
All pain undone
With the warmth of the sun
Eternal and free
We are not victims of the world we see
But powerful and holy as Love sets us free

Declan Lynch

RESOURCES

Your local GP or Memory Clinic will have a list of services available to you locally.

NB: Be aware many of the resources you are given by statutory personnel may only lead to a telephone helpline.

Power of Attorney
https://www.gov.uk/goverment/publications/make-a-lasting-power-of-attorney

Age UK
https://www.ageuk.org.uk/information-advice/health-wellbeing/conditions-illnesses/dementia/

Citizens Advice
https://www.citizensadvice.org.uk/about-us/contact-us/contact-us/contact-us/

Admiral Nursing
https://www.dementiauk.org/get-support/dementia-helpline-alzheimers-helpline/

Attendance Allowance
https://www.gov.uk/attendance-allowance

Carer's Allowance
https://www.gov.uk/carers-allowance

Carer's Assessment
https://www.nhs.uk/conditions/social-care-and-support-guide/support-and-benefits-for-carers/carer-assessments/

Council Tax
https://www.gov.uk/apply-council-tax-reduction

Disability Benefit
https://www.gov.uk/browse/benefits/disability

Free training for carers
https://promas.co.uk/

Carers UK
https://www.carersuk.org/

Alzheimer's
www.alzheimers.org.uk

Purple Angel's charity for free MP3 players
https://purpleangel-global.com/

Sunflower Lanyard—they really do create a different level of understanding from the public of a hidden disability https://freestuff.co.uk/free-sunflower-hidden-disability-lanyard/

Memory Choirs
https://www.musicalmemorieschoir.co.uk/

ACTIVITY IDEAS

Excellent resource
https://sunflowercommunities.org/news/activities-for-people-with-dementia/

https://www.nhs.uk/conditions/dementia/activities/

https://www.alzheimers.org.uk/get-support/staying-independent/activity-ideas-dementia

Raizer Lift
https://raizer.us/products/raizer-ii/

SUGGESTED READING AND VIEWING

Contented Dementia by Oliver James
https://contenteddementiatrust.org/

Teepa Snow—I learnt so many useful techniques by watching the online videos
https://teepasnow.com